AN AVALON CAREER ROMANCE

A TRADE WIND SEASON
Kathleen Mix

The idea of spending the winter working in a tropical paradise is too tantalizing for Melissa Catterly to resist. On an impulse, she accepts a job as a gourmet chef aboard a sixty-five foot sailing yacht bound for the Caribbean.

When the boat sets sail on an eight-day trip from North Carolina to the Virgin Islands, she and Hunt Stewart, the charismatic captain, are strangers. Love has never been kind to Melissa and she resolves to remain only his shipmate and friend. Hunt is devoted to the boat and the sea and not inclined to compromise his lifestyle.

But through their time working together in the ship's close quarters and taking excursions to beautiful, pristine beaches, they begin to form a close bond and deep affection for each other. Melissa has a secret, though, that could tear them apart forever. She can only hope that the tropical trade winds bring good fortune and not more heartache.

A TRADE WIND SEASON

•

Kathleen Mix

AVALON BOOKS
NEW YORK

PRINTED IN THE UNITED STATES OF AMERICA
ON ACID-FREE PAPER
BY HADDON CRAFTSMEN, BLOOMSBURG, PENNSYLVANIA

To Dave, my husband and shipmate, with love

Chapter One

Melissa's pulse was racing. She told herself again that she was doing the right thing. It couldn't hurt if she just took one quick look. And it was now or never.

In her heart she believed that Mr. Barnes would have wanted her to do this. In her mind she knew that she needed answers to her nagging questions. Was there something special here she was meant to discover, some secret formula for finding the kind of joy he had derived from life? His spirit seemed to be guiding her, and she let it lead the way.

But now that she was here, she had to pause for a minute to calm her nerves. She stood motionless, concentrating her senses on the day and the place.

It was a beautiful morning and the combination of the warm North Carolina sun and a cool autumn

1

breeze felt like a caress on Melissa's face. Her hair lifted and twirled in the breeze. She reached up and gathered some of it into a barrette to keep it under control. The thick black strands felt warm to her touch as she smoothed them down to the center of her back. The salt air blew in from the sea, and she closed her eyes and breathed deeply of the scent. The tingling sensations sparked a flood of memories of the days when her mother would bring her to the beach to romp in the surf and build elaborate sandcastles on the shore. From above, she heard the plaintive cries of gray and white gulls that circled lazily, casting shadows on the dock.

Melissa felt sad memories of Mr. Barnes's death sneaking into her mind and inhaled sharply, determined not to let anything spoil this magical place. She'd handled these feelings before, and she would manage them again now.

Raising her narrow chin slightly, she forged ahead, striding through the Atlantic Shores Yacht Club searching for E Dock. Finally she found it, the farthest one from the entrance, next to the wide main channel. In the distance she could see several marshy islands of sawgrass scattered haphazardly in a maze of smaller creeks. The wind bent the tall stalks gently to its will, and the water swirled around their roots. A sailboat with coppery-red sails glided slowly across the horizon. Melissa's nerves tensed and she turned from the concrete walkway onto the gray, weathered dock boards. Halfway down and tied alongside, was a much larger sailboat. On the stern, painted in six-inch high black script lettering and outlined in gold leaf, was the name: *Whitecap.*

She squeezed her eyelids shut to prevent the salty tears welling in her eyes from spilling free. The grief of Mr. Barnes's death that she had barricaded inside struggled toward the surface, but she forced it out of her thoughts by focusing on the sailboat.

Whitecap. Mr. Barnes's beloved *Whitecap.* She wasn't really sure what she had expected, but he had been right. The boat was lovely. The graceful white hull was smooth and shiny, and rays of dappled sunlight, reflected up by tiny wavelets, danced upon it in fanciful patterns. She shaded her eyes and gazed up at the tall masts that seemed to reach almost to the puffy clouds rushing past. She had only come for a quick look, but now she couldn't leave without seeing more. Mr. Barnes had wanted her here on this boat. She felt compelled to find out why.

Holding tightly to the sun-bleached wooden handrail, Melissa inched her way up the narrow gangplank and stepped aboard. She took a few steps forward and looked around her. Brightly varnished wood rails on the cabin top sparkled golden and reflected sunlight into her eyes. Neatly coiled lines hung in orderly fashion at the base of the towering masts. Smooth, polished fittings contrasted with the grainy texture of the scrubbed teakwood deck.

The slight rocking motion beneath her feet sent her mind speeding back to Mr. Barnes. He had described it all to her so well. The waves sending spray into the air at the bow, the wind puffing out the sails. She could picture it now and hear his voice again, telling her tales of his adventures. Somehow, standing on the deck of the boat he had loved, she was able to remember him as alive and happy. She smiled to herself, thankful for that memory and satisfied that her trip here had been worthwhile.

Someone behind her cleared his throat.

Melissa started and her hand instinctively flew to cover her heart as she spun around toward the sound. Her gaze came to rest on a sun-bronzed, muscular man. His broad shoulders were just above the level of her chin and blended perfectly with his trim but powerful appearance. He seemed as much a part of the boat as the masts or decks or sails. He had strong, masculine features and her eyes were drawn to his face, which was handsomely weathered by the wind. As she stared, he slipped a pair of dark sunglasses over his sky-blue eyes.

She remembered that Morgan had told her the captain might be on board and had warned her to stay away.

"Sorry," he said. "I didn't mean to startle you. But this is a private yacht."

His fine, wheat-colored hair had the look of having been bleached by the sun. The smooth baritone voice made her heart miss several beats. "I know that, I'm . . . ah, here because of . . . to see . . ."

His eyebrows arched above his glasses. "I don't suppose you came to deliver sails, did you?"

"Why . . . no, I didn't."

"Well, if you're not from the sail loft, then I probably need to know whether or not you can make a great rum punch," he said.

She tried to focus on his words, but her heart was pounding much too fast and her face was burning from the embarrassment of being discovered. "I beg your pardon?"

He frowned and repeated the question. "A rum punch. Can you mix one?"

"Yes, of course," she answered, silently trying to plan her escape. "Why?"

"It's a favorite with our customers. Haven't you worked as a charter cook before?"

"Ah . . . no, I haven't." She frowned and looked away. *A charter cook?*

When she looked back, he was standing with one hand resting on his hip and his sunglasses removed. His eyes slid from her face downward over her emerald-green blouse and past her snug-fitting jeans.

She tensed under his inspection. Her brain searched for an appropriate cutting remark to put him in his place.

He stopped the evaluation abruptly at her shoes. His expression changed to a look of annoyance. Then he leaned to look past her, as if scanning for damage on the surface of the smooth teak deck.

"Did you go any farther forward in those hard-soled shoes?"

His tone unnerved her. "No. I stopped right here."

"I suppose that's something to be thankful for," he muttered.

Melissa watched the growing irritation on his face. When he continued with his questions his voice was businesslike. "Can you fry plantain chips without getting them greasy?"

Melissa had never fried plantains. But gourmet restaurants had competed for her culinary skills. Of course, she could handle anything so basic. Her pride and something about the way he asked the question, more like a challenge than an inquiry, made her stand a little stiffer and answer yes. Then she realized he was testing her, and she became intent on his questions. The competitive side of her nature had never been able to resist a challenge. And she was sure that was exactly what this was.

He crossed his arms and narrowed his eyes. "Can you plan meals that conform to a diabetic diet?"

That was easy. Mr. Barnes had been diabetic. "Yes, I'm very familiar with the requirements." If he was going to quiz her on her knowledge of dietetics she felt smugly confident of her expertise.

"What about vegetarian?"

She raised her chin, then reached up and tossed a few stray locks of hair back over her shoulder. "No problem. Nutrition was my favorite subject in school."

He raised an eyebrow. "School?"

"U.N.C.W. and the Bambridge Culinary Institute," she explained with a note of victory in her voice.

He paused a few seconds and drummed his fingers on his muscular upper arm. "University of North Carolina . . . ?"

"At Wilmington. Sorry, I guess you're not from around here, are you?" She tried to be pleasant, thinking that she would change the subject and put an end to this silly inquisition, then slip away.

"No, Connecticut, originally." He nodded and pursed his lips. "But I have heard of Bambridge. So, how do you feel about down-to-earth food like brownies? Cake-like or chewy? And what about nuts?" His stance revealed a crack in his armor.

She was amused by the question, but she suppressed a smile and answered with mock seriousness. "Definitely chewy, with walnuts, or, better still, pecans." From the look on his face, she could tell she had scored some points. And she was sure she knew where one vulnerable nerve ending was hiding.

He creased his brow in a frown. "You use any drugs at all?"

"Definitely not."

"Good. This boat is drug free for the crew and the charter guests, no exceptions. The Coast Guard has a zero tolerance policy and so do I. Understood?"

It seemed like a logical idea. "Yes."

"Do you have a valid passport?"

"Yes." She shifted her weight from one foot to the other. She was growing impatient with his interrogation, but his commanding presence seemed to hold her there, and, strangely, she wasn't anxious to be dismissed.

He started pacing in short laps. "Good. A birth certificate is acceptable, but a passport speeds things up. Almost every week we have to clear customs in and out of the British half of the Virgins Islands. When we get back to the U.S.V.I., you'll need to prove to immigration that you're a citizen."

He lifted his dark sunglasses toward his face, but paused before he put them on. He briefly studied her and seemed satisfied with what he saw. Then he slid another glance at her feet. "Well, I guess you'll have to do, then. You can get your things aboard tonight. I want to shove off as soon as possible. Whenever the sails are delivered, we'll go."

He seemed so sure of himself, that Melissa took uncharacteristic pleasure in disagreeing. "I doubt that. Nothing about this conversation makes any sense."

He sighed, shook his head slowly side to side and then smiled. "Great. You mean Roger didn't fill you in?" He didn't wait for a reply. "Okay. In a nutshell, I've got a charter that starts two weeks from today in St. Thomas. The sails haven't come back from the sailmaker yet, and four days ago my cook quit. I need a combination gourmet cook and general crewmember, fast. And then I need to get out of here and down to the Virgin Islands, pronto. We spend the winter season in the Caribbean and, if this lady doesn't get sold out from under us, next summer in New England.

Mostly Newport, Rhode Island. So, what do you think? You want the job or not?"

She smiled slightly. *It's been a long time since I had an interview, but at least I haven't lost my touch.* She opened her mouth to answer no to his job offer, but something about the way he looked into her eyes jolted her to a stop. Gulls soared overhead carefree and gay, and suddenly she was very interested in this position. *A job as cook and crew on* Whitecap! Spending the winter in the Virgin Islands was a tantalizing idea. Mr. Barnes had claimed the V.I. had the most beautiful beaches in the world.

She thought about the few times she had attempted to sail a tiny Optimist pram as a child. Several times her brother had tried to teach her, but she was never able to grasp the concepts.

"I'm not much of a sailor," she ventured.

He frowned again. His golden hair was cut slightly longer than was fashionable and got caught in the breeze and danced in the sunlight. It seemed to provide the perfect contrast to the lines of seriousness she noticed embedded in his brow.

"You don't get seasick, do you?"

He asked the question as if he were speaking of a dread disease, she thought. "No, nothing like that."

"Well, then, the rest of it's a piece of cake. I only really need a hand once in a while. She's pretty much set up to sail single-handed. If you can whip up meals that will keep the charter guests happy, I can handle *Whitecap.* So, when can you be aboard?"

Her mind was reeling. She came here to put the past to rest, once and for all. But maybe this would be even better. If she took the job she'd be working, doing something to get her mind off her grief, replacing her memories of Mr. Barnes's last days with visions of him when he was young and alive. She hadn't looked for another job since his death, so she had no commitments to stop her. Melissa made an instant decision. "Tomorrow morning."

His face broke into a wonderful, boyish grin that she guessed had broken more than a few hearts.

"One more thing," he said. "Let's get it straight right now. You and I will have a strictly professional relationship. We each have our own cabins, and we respect each other's privacy. We work together as crew on this boat, that's it. Clear?"

Melissa bristled. *The man certainly has no ego problems. Sure, he's attractive. But does he really think every woman he meets is going to swoon at his feet?* She had spent many years purposefully avoiding any man she might be tempted to love in order to protect herself from being hurt. She certainly wasn't about to fall for a handsome sailor who probably had at least one woman in every port.

"Very clear, thank you. In fact, I wouldn't be interested in the job if you thought otherwise."

He laughed and extended his right hand. "Good. Glad to hear you say that. It never hurts to get everything out into the open. It's a little late, but I'm Hunt Stewart. Welcome aboard. And you're . . . ?"

Morgan's warning echoed in her mind but she shrugged off his words. "Melissa. Melissa Catterly." She shook Hunt's hand, watching his face for a reaction to her name. She breathed easier when she saw there was none.

He gripped her hand for half a moment longer than was necessary. She stood awkwardly, waiting for him to let go but content to enjoy the pervading warmth of his touch. Flustered, she dropped her eyes, hiding the sudden jumbled feelings that swept through her. Then she pulled her hand away and ran her fingers through her bangs, fluffing them.

"Okay, Melissa, be back in the morning." His eyes slid downward to her feet again. "And throw out those shoes, will you?"

She bit her lip and resisted the urge to balk at his request. He was barefoot and she guessed that maybe her shoes were revealing her nautical ignorance. Besides, she told herself, you have to get used to the idea that he's the captain. And deferring to his judgement about the type of shoes that you should wear is a small price to pay for a chance to reorganize your life.

"I'll consider it. Oh, and by the way, Bambridge graduates are chefs, not cooks."

His mouth twitched upward at the corners. "I'll try to remember that."

She promised to be aboard early, climbed off the boat and walked self-consciously away down the dock.

As she moved through the yacht club toward the exit, she had the uneasy feeling that the captain was watching her. You're imagining it, she told herself. But she couldn't shake the feeling that his eyes were on her back. Finally, unable to control her curiosity any longer, she turned and glanced across the docks and back toward the deck of the sailboat. Her eyes met his. He reached up and touched the brim of a nonexistent cap in a mock salute. A tingle shot down her spine, and she turned and rushed through the exit.

Chapter Two

Driving home, Melissa twisted her mouth into a wry grin. By indulging her curiosity she had just accepted a job working on a boat that might soon belong to her. She wondered what Mr. Barnes would have thought of that. She decided he probably would have chuckled then launched into a story that, he would say, reminded him of a similar experience in his younger years. She wished he was still here telling those stories and bit her lip, fighting back her pain and tears.

Her mind replayed the two and a half years that she had worked for him before he died. He had become like a father to her, taking the place of the natural father she'd never known. She thought about the many times she'd sat with him, holding his hand as he tried to fight off the malignant disease that was consuming his body, and listened as he told her tales of his sailing adventures in the West Indies. His favorite subject had always been his beloved boat: *Whitecap*.

She remembered how shocked she'd been when she'd learned that he'd left the sixty-five foot sailboat to her in his will. And how, when she'd found out the boat was temporarily docked nearby, she'd felt compelled to see it, like a fan longing to meet the heroine of a favorite novel.

As she turned the faded blue sedan left onto Market Street, she glanced at her feet and wondered what was wrong with her shoes. Her uneasiness over making such a drastic change in her life turned to amusement over the captain's request. Finally, though, it was the echo of Mr. Barnes's chuckle in the silence of her heart that reinforced her decision.

"Why shouldn't I do it?" she said aloud. "If he loved those islands so much, then maybe I should experience them, too. I need a change and a new perspective. I need to find some meaning in my life again. Just this once, I'm going to be impulsive and daring. I'm going to follow the whisper of instinct rather than the arguments of reason."

She smiled. *Now I'll have a purpose again, and an exciting one at that.*

Mentally, she started making a detailed list of all the things she needed to do if she was going to move aboard the boat by morning.

* * *

A loud rap on the hull brought Hunt out of the engine room. He grabbed a rag and wiped the oil from his hands as he climbed on deck. On the dock, Roger was busy removing his shoes. His frame was so tall and lanky that, standing on one foot, he reminded Hunt of a heron fishing in the shallows. The wind lifted a few tufts of dark wavy hair on the top of his head, adding to the illusion.

After his shoes were off, Roger stiffly saluted. "Permission to come aboard, sir," he joked.

Hunt smiled at the jab, reminded that, years ago, Roger had been the captain and Hunt the crew. "Just what I need, a low-life boarding party." He struck a more serious note. "I don't suppose you brought sails with you?"

Roger came onboard and settled in the cockpit, stretching his long, thin legs all the way across. "No, but I've got good news. They'll be ready tomorrow. Just thought I'd stop by and see how you're doing otherwise. Sorry about striking out on the cook."

"What do you mean?" Hunt asked, sitting across from him.

"I mean, I contacted everyone I know between here and Savannah and there isn't a good charter cook available anywhere. I'll keep looking, of course, but you'll probably have to pick one up after you get down to St. Thomas. For a high enough price there's always somebody willing to switch ships."

"What about Melissa?"

Roger looked puzzled. "Who?"

Hunt was confused. "Melissa." He sat up straight and peered at Roger. "Wait a minute. Are you telling me you didn't send her?"

Roger shrugged his shoulders and spread his bony hands. "I haven't sent anyone. The girl who was supposed to come in this morning cancelled."

"Well, I'll be . . ." Hunt muttered. "When she showed up, I just assumed you were responsible."

Roger still looked perplexed. "You mean you've got a cook?"

"I hope so," Hunt replied, shaking his head and sighing.

"Where did she come from? Another boat?"

"I haven't the faintest idea," Hunt admitted. He slumped back against the soft, canvas-covered seat cushions. "I thought that you sent her, so I didn't even ask for references. I figured anyone who got by you must be qualified. She did say she went to Bambridge Culinary Institute. Of course, she didn't exactly look like a boat person—you know, kind of pale, hard-soled shoes—but then again, I didn't have a lot of choices."

Roger gave a short laugh. "If she's really a Bambridge chef I would have hired her in a heartbeat myself, boat person or not." He shrugged. "Maybe she heard about the opening from the yacht club office or her own networking."

"I suppose. She did sound like she knows her way around food, and that's what's most important."

Roger smirked. "I keep telling you half of our customers are lured by my glowing descriptions of the gourmet meals. If they just wanted to sail, there are lots of other boats where they could do it cheaper."

Hunt stretched his tanned arm across the top of the cushions and sighed in resignation. He thought about the future and lines of worry creased his forehead. "This whole trip could turn out to be an exercise in futility, anyhow. It might not matter at all if, like you said the other day, the boat gets put up for sale. I'm going to miss old Mr. Barnes. He was a great boss. Any more word on the estate?"

"No," Roger answered, shaking his head. "But I'll keep trying to find out what's going on. All I know for sure is that his son is contesting the will."

"He's got to be livid. Especially about the idea of the boat getting sold."

Roger sat up and slapped Hunt's knee. "Come on, cheer up, she's not sold yet. And even if *Whitecap* does get put up for sale, it doesn't necessarily mean that she'll get sold out of the charter business. Maybe a new owner would want to keep things just as they are. You never know. They could even want you to stay on as captain. Not that I could see why." He laughed. "Come on, let's go over to the Islander and grab something to eat. There's no use worrying about things that may never happen."

Hunt shrugged. "Yeah, I guess you're right. Are you sure about the sails?"

"They promised me tomorrow."

Hunt got to his feet. "That would be perfect timing.

Melissa—whoever she is—is moving onboard in the morning. All the maintenance work is done. And I'm really itching to get out of here. A week tied to a dock is about all I can take."

Roger chuckled. "Someday you may have to get used to it. I did."

"Impossible. There's no way I could ever bury the anchor," Hunt told Roger as they left the boat and started down the dock. "Even if *Whitecap* gets sold out from under me, I could never give up the sea. There's too much water out there that I haven't sailed yet. And I don't intend to miss any of it."

Melissa checked the time on her watch. It was two o'clock already, and she had a standing date with Morgan at seven. She decided her first priority should be to find some information about sailboats. Wilmington was a large boating center and there were three marine supply stores listed in the telephone directory. She copied all three addresses from the book.

At the first store, she struck pay dirt. Half an hour after she got there, she left with her arms loaded with how-to books and glossy-covered sailing magazines. At the second store, she bought a pair of taupe-leather deck shoes.

"Soft soled shoes are an absolute necessity," the salesman told her, in response to her question. "Preferably with a non-skid pattern. With the shoes you're wearing you'd be slipping over the side in no time or possibly damaging expensive woodwork."

She thought about Hunt's bare feet, and now, understood his motives.

Later, she stopped at the Used Book Emporium and found a real treasure, an encyclopedia of Caribbean fruits and vegetables. She was sure that the islands would have foods that were unavailable in the States and that a good reference book would be invaluable for experimenting with new recipes and flavors.

Her next concern was clothing. In the past, she had always worn white uniforms when she was working. Now, flipping rapidly through an issue of *Sail* magazine, she analyzed the shortcomings of her summer wardrobe and got some hints from the pictures about what to wear on a boat. A quick stop at a trendy sportswear boutique added an irresistible sundress, two additional pairs of shorts, and some extras to her T-shirt collection. She puzzled over a tiny white bikini that was probably never meant to touch the water. Finally, feeling a little giddy, she bought it, just in case. Then she rushed home. Packing still loomed ahead and she needed to change for dinner.

Melissa arrived at the restaurant a few minutes early and decided to wait in the lounge. Smoothing the fabric as she sat, she realized this was the same dress she'd worn the night of her first date with Morgan. It was a straight, oriental style of pale green silk with a line of fabric-covered buttons that went up one side and then across her shoulder to the mandarin collar. That night, he had joked that with her black hair hanging loose, and the style of her dress, they should have gone to a Chinese restaurant to eat. She regretted wearing it again now.

She ordered a glass of ginger ale, munched on some cheese cubes from the happy hour buffet, and sat listening to the tinkling notes of the piano. The tune was vaguely familiar but she couldn't match a name with the melody. Soon she gave up and was content to just absorb the mood. In a few minutes, the slow, relaxing music helped her adjust her state of mind after her hectic afternoon. Morgan was late as usual, but tonight she was glad to have some time to catch her breath and think.

At seven-thirty, Morgan rushed through the door and wove smoothly through the crowded room to where she sat. As usual, he wore a smartly tailored three-piece suit. Tonight, it was dark blue and blended nicely with a lighter blue shirt and a conservative red striped tie. His chestnut brown hair was, of course, combed neatly to one side and perfectly in place. She smiled as he approached. In all the time she'd known him she had never seen him look ruffled or upset. He was always the perfect picture of a successful, corporate lawyer.

He ordered a Scotch and water and, as they waited for a table, launched into a lively description of the events of his day that she knew would continue most of the way through dinner.

Minutes after they were seated and had ordered, the waiter served their spinach and mandarin orange salad.

Melissa knew that Peter, the chef here, liked to use unique combinations of herbs and spices in his creations. She closed her eyes and let her taste buds bathe in the citrus vinaigrette dressing, trying to identify each flavor and guess the proportions of each ingredient.

"This is excellent," she commented.

Morgan had eaten his rapidly. "I was too starved to notice to tell you the truth. I worked through lunch."

She ate slowly as he continued to talk. When the entrée was served, Melissa considered the arrangement of the slices of marinated tenderloin and the paté-stuffed mushroom caps drizzled with raspberry demi-glace on her plate and decided that the sprig of parsley for garnish didn't add enough color. A few petals of yellow nasturtium blossom could heighten the appeal. But otherwise the aroma was robust and the plate was hot. She cut a small piece of the meat, noted the pink interior, and chewed discriminatingly. It was tender, juicy, and cooked just right.

"I went to see *Whitecap* today," she announced at last.

He frowned. "And?"

She smiled warmly. "You know me so well, don't you? Yes, there's more." She inhaled deeply. "I'm leaving for a while, Morgan. I'm going to work as crew on the boat and sail to the Caribbean."

His eyes rolled upward. "That's not even close to being funny. You'd better tell me what happened."

"I went to see the boat and went aboard. I was only

going to stay a minute but then the captain came out and caught me."

"I was afraid of that."

"I know. But he didn't know who I was. And he thought I was there to apply for a job as chef. After we talked for a few minutes, he offered me the position. And I accepted."

"Did you tell him your name?"

"Yes."

"Well, it might have been better if you just made up something but if he didn't recognize it . . . hopefully he won't connect you with the will."

"Even if he does, I still don't see why it should matter."

"It matters. Trust me. Sometimes practicing law is like playing a game of chess. And I don't want opposing council to know any of our moves. We have a strong position right now."

"But his son can never prove Mr. Barnes was incompetent. He was sharp right up until the day he died."

He reached out and put his hand over hers. "Listen, Melissa, I wouldn't have made out his will if I didn't believe he was competent. But Mr. Barnes was eccentric, and you have to admit that sometimes his behavior was strange. Unethical lawyers frequently come up with medical experts who will testify to half-truths for the right fee. Right now they're trying to pressure us into giving up your claim by hinting that they can produce those experts. As I said yesterday, I just don't want you near the boat. Don't give them any ideas or ammunition. Anyway, playing along with the captain was probably a good move. Maybe it kept him from getting suspicious."

"I'm going to take the job." An image of Hunt's smiling face and laughing blue eyes floated through her consciousness. "I told the captain I would. I meant it."

"Just call him and tell him you've changed your mind."

"I can't do that."

"Melissa, please, tell me you're kidding. I know how upset you've been since Mr. Barnes's death, but this doesn't make any sense. You're not a deckhand, for heaven's sake. Your place is here with me."

She lowered her eyes to the single white daisy in the milk glass bud vase on the table. A few stray notes from the piano drifted across the candlelit room. "I want to do this, Morgan. I know it sounds crazy, but I feel I have to." She took another deep breath. "I'm not asking you to wait."

He put his hand inside his jacket and brought out a small velvet box. He opened it and placed it before Melissa. "Wait? I want you to marry me, darling. I was going to ask you later, over dessert. But I'm doing it now. Will you?"

"I . . . I don't know, Morgan."

"I love you and I'll make you happy. I know you don't love me, but in time you'll learn to. We'll have a couple babies, become a family."

Tears came to her eyes. "I know you love me," she whispered. "And I want babies too. But I just don't know what to do. I need time to be by myself and think."

She knew it was logical that she should accept his proposal. He was offering her a sense of comfort and security that she had not felt since her childhood. And she was very fond of him. But she couldn't ignore the fact that it wouldn't be fair to him. He should marry someone who would love him in return.

Morgan stared down at the icy stone for a long minute. Finally, he picked it up and, turning her hand over, placed it in her palm. "It's yours, darling. No matter what you decide. Keep it, please. But stay with me here until you make up your mind. Don't go away on this crazy boat trip."

His reaction made her heart feel leaden. The last thing she wanted was to hurt him. A lone tear rolled slowly down her cheek. "I'm sorry. I hope you understand. If I don't go, it wouldn't be fair to either of us. I need to do this, Morgan. It will help me to get over Mr. Barnes's death and give me time to get my life back on track. I think we need some time apart. Marriage is too big a commitment to make unless we're both absolutely sure."

He brushed the tear aside. A look of resignation came to his face. "I'm not positive I do understand, but I suppose I don't have much choice but to respect your decision. When are you leaving?"

"Tomorrow, or the next day. I'm not exactly sure,"

she replied. A weight lifted from her shoulders when she saw his expression of acceptance.

"Are you positive I can't talk you out of this? What if it affects the distribution of the estate?"

She smiled and determination showed in the flashes of light in her gray eyes. Now that she had taken a giant step toward regaining control of her life, she was heartened to keep going. "I don't see how it can. I need a job. The captain needs a chef. So, I spend some time working aboard the boat. Even if they find out, what can the other lawyers possibly make of that?"

"Truthfully, I don't know. But I prefer to be cautious."

"I'll be discreet. I'm not being reckless. I've thought this through and it makes sense financially. *Whitecap* is expensive to own. You said yourself that's why I wouldn't be able to keep her. By saving the salary of one crewmember, I'll be making sure that I have the money available to cover the boat's upkeep until it sells."

"I'm just trying to look out for your interests."

"I know. And I appreciate all you've done for me. But the money this saves can help pay the inheritance taxes, too. You know I can't afford to pay them without wiping out most of my bank account."

"Will you keep in touch?" he asked. He took a deep breath, then spoke like a lawyer. "If not for me, at least to let us finish up the details of the estate?"

Melissa leaned over the table and lightly kissed his

cheek. "Of course I will," she promised. "You're very special to me."

His eyes were not the eyes of a detached lawyer any longer. "I'd like to be more than special, darling."

She looked into his eyes and saw his sadness. "All I can promise you is that I'll think about you often. Who knows, maybe you'll meet someone else who can make you happy while I'm gone." As she said it, she knew it sounded trite, but no other words came.

After they finished their coffee and left the restaurant, Morgan walked with her to her car. He hesitated, then took her into his arms and tenderly kissed her good-bye. She slipped into the driver's seat and started the engine. They went their separate ways.

Chapter Three

By the next morning, Melissa had accomplished most of the items on her to-do list and her roommate had promised to complete the rest, including putting her car into storage.

Surrounded by her belongings, she stood nervously on the dock. She noticed a small wooden sign attached near the boarding gate. "Soft-soled shoes only," it announced, and "no boarding without permission". She wondered if it had been there yesterday.

Melissa took a deep calming breath and reached out to ring the small buzzer on the portable gangplank. Before she could press the button, someone startled her by stepping up behind her and speaking.

"If you put this mountain of stuff in your cabin, you're not going to have any room to sleep."

She turned and saw Hunt. His forehead was creased in a frown. "It's not that small, is it?"

"I guess you'll just have to bring it all aboard and see."

She saw something like doubt or regret cloud his eyes.

"Are you moving all this stuff off another boat?" he asked.

"As a matter of fact, no. I've been sharing an apartment in town." Here we go again, she thought, another inquisition. She caught the pleasant but unsettling scent of an aftershave that suggested vibrant masculinity.

"Oh? Have you been cooking at a restaurant or something? I understand there's a good supply of gourmet places in this area."

"No. Nothing like that. I've been working at a private estate." He can't change his mind now, she told herself. That wouldn't be fair.

He eyed her with one eyebrow arched high and crossed his arms over his chest. He looked like he was ready to make a decision. Melissa didn't give him a chance to reconsider. She picked up one bulging bag, then another, and started toward the gangplank.

"So, where are my quarters?"

He lifted a stack of her heavily loaded boxes with ease. "Come on, I'll show you."

Melissa followed him aboard the boat, then down below through the companionway.

The spaciousness and elegance of the yacht's interior pleasantly surprised her. Richly varnished wood cabinetry and plush cushions in a muted blue and green print filled the main cabin with a sense of subtle luxury. Polished brass oil lamps, hanging regally between oriental carvings, reflected the golden sunlight that filtered through a smoke-tinted skylight. Planks of warm-brown teak alternated with strips of cream-colored holly in the glossy wood floor, making her glad she was wearing soft-soled shoes. The decor had an aura of masculinity that, she presumed, was to be expected on a boat, but it was tastefully done with enough softening accents to appeal to a woman.

She followed Hunt along a narrow corridor until he turned and entered a tiny room. Then he stopped and stacked her boxes on the floor. The cabin that was to be her new home was small but inviting and gave her an immediate impression of comfort. The same blues and greens used in the main cabin were carried through in the cheerful decor. Along the length of the room, against the hull, she saw a narrow bunk with a puffy blue comforter wedged between attractive varnished cabinetry. Just above the bunk, sunlight streamed in through a large round port providing ample light. An arched doorway on one end of the room opened to a tiny private shower. On the other end, a small closet had been artfully squeezed into the only remaining space.

"Here we are," Hunt said. "I'll bring the rest of your stuff aboard. You can start figuring out where you think it's all going to go."

When he returned with the biggest box, he set it down and remarked, "Sounds like something's broken in there."

Melissa opened it and looked inside. A potted plant had fallen over. She picked it up and pushed the soil back around the stems.

"Plants? We don't have room for a garden," he said, sounding incredulous.

"We have to. I can't be expected to prepare pesto without fresh basil."

"Basil?"

She handed him two pots. "Basil and Italian parsley." She stooped and picked up two more. "Thyme and oregano." She indicated the last three. "Rosemary, mint and chives."

"Okay, okay. I guess you can put them in the galley." He rolled his eyes toward the overhead, and shook his head. "Anything, for pesto." Then, smiling, he turned and left.

He returned twice more, loaded down with boxes. When he finished, he told her, "Make yourself at home. You can put together some lunch later, and we'll get better acquainted then. I'll be on deck polishing the stainless. Just yell if you need anything." His eyes scanned the pile of boxes once more. Then he walked away, shaking his head again.

For a moment, she stood with a smile on her face, letting her imagination mix a tropical evening with the lingering scent of aftershave in the room. Then she shook off her musings and began the formidable task of unpacking. It's a good thing clothing for warm weather is light, she thought. The space in her cabin was sufficient, but just barely. Every drawer and shelf was quickly filled.

After she finished stowing her belongings, she wandered through the boat for a few minutes, absorbing the friendliness of the main salon and peeking through the open doors of the sleeping cabins. Then she strolled to the well-equipped galley and explored the many cabinets and ingenious storage areas, taking note of the available cooking utensils and inventorying the food supplies. At noon, she began preparing lunch.

She found that cooking in the confines of the small galley would take some practice, but she was pleased with the efficiency and neatness of the layout. A three-burner, propane-fueled stove with a compact oven sat on one side of the U-shaped cabin, a large refrigerator/ freezer spread over the other side. A deep, gleaming, stainless steel sink was nestled in between. Counter space was a little limited but she was sure she could learn to manage.

She served lunch in the cockpit under the welcome shade of the broad white sun awning. Hunt appraised the meal and, sampling the creamy salad dressing, nodded his approval. "With no charter guests aboard, I tend to stock the boat with foods that I like. When I thought I might be making my own meals I avoided everything but simple items. I'm really impressed with what you've managed to concoct out of nothing. This is delicious."

"Thank you," she murmured, at the same time wondering why she had been so eager to please him.

Soon, he finished the last crumb of the quiche crust and dug into the warm peach cobbler with whipped cream. "Did you find everything you need in the galley? We can have an order delivered from the grocery this afternoon if you want anything special."

She thought for a second. "Well, the freezer is very well stocked and the canned goods supply is better than some stores I've been in. But there's a shortage of fresh vegetables, your yeast is almost out-of-date, and, of course, you're out of sour cream and yogurt."

Hunt twisted his mouth into a grimace. "Yogurt? You don't actually eat that awful stuff. Do you?"

Melissa stiffened. "Yes, I do. Most days for lunch in fact. It's very nutritious."

Hunt shook his head. "Well, if you want some, get it. But there are two things I hate and yogurt's one of them. Don't put any of it near me."

Her tone was sarcastic. "Are vegetables the other?"

"Not all of them, just okra." His eyes had an amused sparkle. "Maybe you've got to be from the South to like it. But being a Yankee, it always seems sort of slippery to me. Actually, grits are second on my list. They remind me of lumpy paste."

Melissa didn't respond. *He's baiting me. Purposely trying to see if I'll argue with him. This is probably a test to see if I can get along with the charterers.* She smiled sweetly. "I'll remember that." They ate in silence for several minutes.

"The sails will be back this afternoon," he said finally, "so we ought to be able to shove off in the morning."

"How long does it take to get to St. Thomas?" Melissa asked and then immediately regretted the question. She probably should already know that, she chastised herself.

Hunt raised an eyebrow. "Seven days, maybe eight at the most. Depends on the winds, of course, but the forecast for the next few days is good. They're predicting some brisk westerlies, which should push us along pretty quickly, at least until we hit the trade winds. Then, if we're at the right longitude, we should have a great reach south. I usually figure on making two hundred miles a day as a conservative estimate in those conditions."

Melissa remembered reading that the Virgin Islands were located in an area where easterly trade winds blow almost constantly all year round. And that it is those persistent, predictable winds that cool the islands during the summer months and provide outstanding sailing throughout the winter season. The book described them as an unstoppable force of nature that had been blowing since before the first sailors ventured to sea in ancient boats.

"How fast can *Whitecap* sail?" she asked.

Hunt beamed with enthusiasm as he talked about the boat he loved. "She flies like the wind. Once she settles over on a slight heel and picks up her skirts she just takes off. It's like she's skipping over the water.

Hull speed is about ten and a half knots. I promise you'll see lots of that."

The excitement in his eyes lingered as he asked Melissa, "While we're on the subject, can you navigate at all?"

"No. I'm sorry. I can't."

Hunt nodded his head as if he'd anticipated her answer. "Well, no big problem, I guess. I'll show you some of the easy stuff later. I usually take care of most of it myself anyhow. I'll do the position fixes at the end of your watch."

Navigating? My watch? Fixes? Melissa's head was spinning. *Maybe I've gotten myself in too deep after all.* As she finished the rest of her lunch, she struggled not to be overwhelmed by all there was to learn about boats and sailing.

"Let's go through as much as we can about the boat's systems this afternoon while I do my final checkout," he said. "There's a lot of things you'll need to know."

"I'm sure there probably is," Melissa agreed, then chewed her lip. She began to stack the dishes. Thoughts of the countless lunches she had shared with Mr. Barnes distracted her for an instant and she paused, lost in her vivid memories. When she glanced back up, Hunt was watching her. His gaze made her feel flustered, and she hurried below wondering what he was thinking behind those questioning and unsettling eyes.

Three hours passed quickly as Hunt inspected every

inch of the boat and explained each item to Melissa. He started in the bilges, demonstrating how each of the pumps could be started in an emergency. She watched as he checked the level of oil in the diesel engine and helped as he re-stowed gear. She learned where everything from the monogrammed linens to the spare light bulbs was stored. He demonstrated how to use the VHF marine radio and made a call to check its operation. As Hunt turned on each of the electronic instruments used for navigation, he showed her where to find the instruction booklet. On deck, there was even more information to absorb and she was beginning to feel as she had in college when cramming for an exam.

As she became aware of how complex a boat could be, she began to understand just how much there was to learn. But she found the flood of information that Hunt poured on her fascinating. And hearing the pride and affection in his voice, Melissa realized that maintaining the boat wasn't a chore for Hunt, it was a labor of love.

Late in the day, a man appeared slowly pushing a cart heaped with bulging sail bags down the dock.

"Well, it's about time," Hunt remarked in the manner of a friendly greeting. "Heave them up here and let's get to it."

"Not until you introduce me," the man insisted, nodding toward Melissa.

Hunt smiled. "Roger, Melissa. Melissa, Roger. Now throw me a sail."

Roger stared at Melissa for so long that she began to feel self-conscious. "Extremely pleased to meet you, Melissa. Do they call you Missy?"

Roger. All of a sudden his name registered in her brain and she remembered Hunt's reference to him yesterday. When she glanced at Hunt, their eyes met. His eyes sparkled in amusement. *He's enjoying this. He must already know Roger didn't send me about the job.* But she refused to show her embarrassment and flashed Roger her most charming smile. "Missy or Melissa, either one is fine."

"Well, Missy it is then." He jumped aboard and reached for her hand. When he bowed and kissed her fingertips, she felt a blush warm her cheeks. Yet, at the same time, she immediately liked his unconventional ways.

Hunt stepped beside them and tapped him on the shoulder. "If you don't mind, Don Juan, we've got work to do."

"Sure thing, Cap'n," Roger quipped, snapping to attention. "I can see why you want her all for yourself."

Hunt flashed him a disapproving scowl. Then he leaped to the dock and heaved the largest sail bag directly at Roger. "You gonna earn your dinner or not?"

It was well after dark before all of the sails were rigged to their booms. Hunt and Roger sank into the cockpit cushions, tired but satisfied that everything was done properly. Melissa went below to the galley in search of refreshments.

Roger's gaze followed her, then he turned toward Hunt. "How come I can't be lucky enough to be sailing off to the Caribbean with a gorgeous lady like that?"

Hunt smiled wryly. Being alone on the boat with an attractive woman wasn't always a source of enjoyment. It had, in the past, caused unwanted complications in his life. "You make it sound as if we're going off on some kind of a pleasure cruise. We work together, remember? I need a cook and crew and she fits the bill, that's all there is to it. I can't afford the luxury of looking too closely."

"Well, if you haven't noticed she's a knockout, you must be dead," Roger continued with a mocking smile.

"I didn't say, I didn't notice." Hunt corrected him. "Under other circumstances, yeah, I'll admit I could find her attractive. But the way things are, I have no choice. She's a skilled chef. That's the only thing I care about." He shook off a vision of the wispy tendrils of hair that curled at her earlobe and brushed against the silk-smooth skin of her neck.

Roger sighed. "Well, I think *I've* met the girl of my dreams."

Hunt gave him a playful punch on the shoulder. "Right. You meet the girl of your dreams twice a day."

They shared a friendly laugh. Then Roger jumped up to help Melissa squeeze a large tray piled with food and drinks out through the companionway. They ate heartily and Roger kept up a steady chatter, telling Melissa anecdotes of his days with Hunt in the Navy and since. He joked about the time when they had crewed on a private yacht and told her a story of playing the soundtrack from *Jaws* over the loud hailer one night while the rest of the crew was skinny-dipping.

By the time he was ready to leave, Melissa begged him to stop. "Please, no more, my cheeks are sore from laughing."

He grinned, raised his eyebrows and twirled an imaginary handlebar mustache. "Well then, my dear, before I go, the question we've all been waiting for. What size do you wear?"

"I don't see where that's any of your business!"

Roger backed up two steps and rephrased the question. "Whoa, don't get upset. I just need to know your sizes so that I can order your uniforms."

Melissa's lips turned up slightly at the edges. "Sorry, I guess I overreacted. What do you need to know?"

"T-shirts, small or medium?"

"Medium."

"Shorts?"

"Nine."

"Shoes?"

"Seven. Safe driver discount on my car insurance, prone to freckles and sunburn, no skeletons in my closet, they wouldn't fit . . ."

Roger laughed and waved his hand for her to stop. "Enough. Enough." He jotted down the information he needed, then said goodnight. "Have a good trip," he called over his shoulder as he walked away.

"I guess I'm going to turn in," Hunt announced when Roger was gone. "Be up and ready to go at six."

Below in her cabin, Melissa undressed and sat on the narrow bed, brushing her hair and recalling the events of the day. As she heard Hunt running water in his shower, she thought for the first time that she was here aboard a boat with a man she had met only yesterday. And that tomorrow they would leave the dock and be alone at sea for over a week.

Her mind raced in all directions. *What if he's an ax murderer? What happened to his previous cook? What if he's incompetent and the boat sinks? What if we're attacked by pirates? What in the world am I doing?*

She got up and made sure her door was locked then, with shaking fingers, turned out the light and climbed into bed.

She whispered quietly, "I wanted adventure, I wanted to travel. Oh, Mr. Barnes, I hope your magical boat isn't *too* exciting for me."

The wavelets lapping at the side of the hull seemed to answer, "Tomorrow you will see, tomorrow you will see."

Chapter Four

They were up in the morning before the first rays of golden sunlight burst over the horizon. Hunt had explained that he wanted to catch the last of the ebbing tide to help them through the inlet, rather than depart later and have to fight against an adverse flooding current.

When the moment came to leave the dock, he started the boat's diesel engine and then handed Melissa a long pole with a hook on one end and gave her instructions.

"Use this against the dock to push the bow out until the current catches us and starts to swing us away."

She went forward and pushed off the dock pole, noticing the tiny whirlpools in the water that was gurgling swiftly past. As soon as the boat was positioned

40

with the force of the water off center, the sleek hull slowly swept out into the channel.

Then Hunt called to her. "Come back here, please, and cast off the stern line when I tell you to."

She hurried to the stern, then picked up the line and held it tightly in her hand, sweating nervously as she waited for his command.

"Okay. Now, cast off." His voice gave a gentle firmness to the order.

She let the line slip smoothly around the cleat on the dock, just as he had demonstrated earlier.

"Make sure it's out of the water," he told her. "We don't want to wrap it around the propeller."

The gap started to open between *Whitecap* and the dock. Hunt pushed the gearshift forward and turned the large steering wheel one full revolution, spinning the boat around until it pointed toward the inlet.

A smile crept across Melissa's face as her view of the yacht club changed and she felt the movement of the boat under her feet. *I'm doing it,* she sang inside her head. *I'm making my first sea voyage.*

She turned around to glance at Hunt. He looked excited, also. Melissa could almost see the muscles in his shoulders relaxing as soon as the marina started to fade into the waterfront collage behind them.

They passed the Coast Guard station and then, as they turned to slip between the stone breakwaters of Masonboro Inlet, Hunt let out a joyous whoop. "Next stop, St. Thomas."

She echoed it in her thoughts. *Yes. St. Thomas.*

They were in the swells of the Atlantic by seven o'clock. A fresh autumn breeze had been blowing off the land all through the night and the resulting waves were small close to shore. But the ocean swells that greeted them were not caused by local winds. These waves had traveled over hundreds of miles of ocean from distant storms, like slowly moving mountains. Gently, they lifted *Whitecap* ten feet skyward, then, just as gently, lowered her down, playing with the big, seaworthy boat like a child's fragile toy.

Steadily, Hunt set one sail after another until a cloud of white dacron reached up to embrace the wind. He pulled each line taut and adjusted its tension with the winches, until the flutter at the edge of the sail disappeared.

Melissa observed Hunt as he worked, matching his activities to the illustrations and descriptions in her books. She decided that only a few of the tasks might be beyond her physical capabilities and that in the future she could be of some help.

She noticed how the muscles in his shoulders and arms flexed, and how easily and gracefully he managed the difficult physical tasks. His movements were like those of a practiced athlete whose body was sleek and healthy.

When he finished, he turned and their eyes collided. He smiled in her direction and the same awareness that had jumbled her thoughts when they first met crept over her again. Only this time, twice as strong.

Soon, *Whitecap* rested her side against the sea and

cut through the velvety blue ocean. They were free of the land and on their way.

Melissa sat entranced as the boat sliced through the boundless expanse of undulating water. In the engineless silence, she listened to the gurgle of their wake and the steady sound of the wind. The sun was fully up and sparkled on the sea before them. The salty breeze blew her hair into disarray. She closed her eyes and luxuriated in the gentle touch of the clean, fresh air. *What a perfect day to begin something new. I've made the right decision to do this. A sea voyage will be just what the doctor ordered. I'll be able to clear my mind and make some sense of my life.*

But by dinnertime, she was having second thoughts about the sea. Once away from land, a steady progression of wind waves began to march down behind them. They grew in size as the hours went by, until *Whitecap* was cascading down each face, sending white foam shooting out beside her and spray flying high into the air. She saw that Hunt was grinning broadly. He seemed to be enjoying the power of the wind and sea and the exhilaration of the speed of the boat beneath them.

Melissa was not as pleased. She went below and braced herself in the galley trying to cook. As the boat rolled, she managed to chop and sauté an onion and some strips of bacon without incident. Peeling and dicing the evasive potatoes, and chopping a wandering stalk of celery, were not as easy. Twice she retrieved a rolling potato from the floor after it somersaulted from the countertop. At one point she narrowly missed slicing her finger instead of her intended target. Finally, giving up, she buckled herself into the restraining belt that would keep her from falling. Then, stirring with one hand and holding on with the other, she simmered the onion, celery, crumpled bacon and potatoes in an inch of water. Several times she was caught off balance when the floor tilted under her feet, and only the belt kept her from being thrown across the boat. She quickly learned how to use the pot retainers to keep the pans from slipping off the stove. But keeping the liquid from sloshing out of the pots was another matter. Once the cream, milk, and clams were added to the mixture, curdling spills practically coated the stovetop.

Finally, successful at last, she scooped the thick clam chowder into deep insulated mugs, wedged a baguette of crusty bread beneath her arm and, weaving up the ladder and across the cockpit like the proverbial drunken sailor, served their meal. She marveled at how easily Hunt steered the large boat with one hand and ate with the other, alternately squeezing his mug or a hunk of bread between his knees. Even eating with two hands she had difficulty.

He smiled at her and complimented her efforts. "This is a great meal, especially considering the conditions. Getting your sea legs while rolling downwind isn't always easy."

"You can say that again," she agreed. Her aching muscles had not been part of her expectations. "I think

I've got bruises in places where I didn't know I had places."

He laughed aloud. "You'll get used to it. I'll reef down a little canvas at dark and that should help a bit. I don't mind pushing her some in the daylight, but I get cautious in the dark when I can't see where I'm going. Many a sleeping whale or floating hunk of debris has spoiled a pleasant trip. Boats have sunk in minutes after hitting all sorts of things out here."

Boats have sunk! Hitting whales! For the first time, Melissa realized that there might be obstacles in the open ocean, but she didn't want him to see her concern. "How comforting." She went back to watching the waves and the seabirds again, only now with a slightly different perspective.

A short time later, halfway through a yawn, she bolted upright. There was a black dot on the horizon. She pointed it out to Hunt.

He peered through the binoculars, then handed them to her. "Looks like company coming," he announced.

Her mind saw pirates. After she put the binoculars to her eyes, she let out a sigh of relief. It was a container-carrying freighter. Within fifteen minutes, the massive ship was less than a quarter mile away. Melissa's mouth dropped open as the monstrous, steel hulk slid by, seemingly close enough to touch. In contrast, the sailboat seemed like nothing more than an insignificant speck.

"These container ships make me real nervous," Hunt told her, mirroring her concern and comforting her somehow. "I always wonder if anyone on their bridge has even looked out and seen us. They could run us down and never even know it. Most of them stay on autopilot all the time. They're supposed to keep a radar watch, but they're pretty lax about it."

Melissa watched the ship pass, grow smaller and smaller as it steamed toward the horizon, and finally, disappear completely from sight. When it was gone, a tiny shiver of fright shot up her spine. *Something as impersonal as an autopilot could cut short my new adventures in a matter of minutes.*

As Hunt had promised, he reduced some sail with one reef when the sun dipped beneath the waves behind them. Melissa was grateful for the slight improvement in the motion.

"I like to do three on, three off, watches overnight," Hunt said. "We'll start at nine tonight because today has been special. But from now on, we're on sea routine around the clock. I expect you to wake me for anything unusual, or if the sea or weather conditions change quickly. Don't leave the cockpit under any circumstances without me on deck. And keep your safety harness clipped on all the time, no exceptions. Any questions?"

Melissa shook her head slowly. "No." He had already answered more questions than she would have ever thought to ask.

Hunt checked his watch. "You've still got some time if you want to grab a quick nap."

"I don't think I could sleep right now," Melissa said, knowing she was too agitated to rest.

He shrugged. "Suit yourself."

At nine, the saloon clock chimed twice and it was her watch. She had dreaded this moment, but now it was here. Hunt locked the wheel in place and engaged the self-steering vane. It was an ingenious system whereby the force of the wind actually steered the boat. Melissa didn't quite understand how it worked but she was happy to have it. Steering looked easy enough when Hunt was behind the wheel, but she had no desire right now to try.

Hunt looked toward her. She sensed that his eyes were questioning whether she could stand a proper watch.

"You shouldn't have any problems," he said. "I'll probably wake up anyway if the wind shifts or our speed changes. All you really need to do is keep a lookout for traffic. Keep an eye on the compass. If this baby starts to wander, let me know. Don't hesitate to wake me. I want to know if anything at all comes up."

Then, suddenly, he was gone. She saw him at the chart table for a minute, plotting an X to mark their position, then the red night-light was extinguished and she was alone in the dark. The soft glow from the instruments barely illuminated the cockpit. While he was near, she had felt safe, confident in his abilities. Alone, she imagined demons everywhere. "We're almost a hundred miles from shore," he had said earlier. Now those words seemed much more frightening. A ghostly reflection of their red and green navigation lights bounced across the waves. The dim glow of the compass light cast eerie shadows around her. A small slice of moon and several stars were the only inter- ruptions of the continuous blackness of space and clouds. Behind them a small semicircle of white foam was lit by their stern light, but that too, quickly gave way to a blackness that matched the sky.

Melissa sat rigid and transfixed by the night until the clock chimed three times and interrupted her thoughts. She had quickly come to understand the sys- tem of one bell or chime for each half-hour, with eight bells at eight, twelve and four o'clock, and the count starting over again with one bell on the half hour after each of those hours. She inched behind the wheel and read the compass. East, ninety degrees, plus or minus five, Hunt had told her. The needle wavered back and forth near the correct numbers. Her heart was pound- ing and she shivered in the evening dampness. *I can do this. I have to.* She scanned around her straining to see, but the murky darkness gave no hint of what per- ils might lurk only a few yards away.

For the first time since his death, she thought of the night she and her brother, Bobby, had slept in a tent when she was seven. For a week, they'd unmercifully begged their mother to allow them to camp in the backyard. She'd finally relented. They were thrilled. It wasn't until after dark that fear set in. Within an hour, Melissa was ready to seek the safety of her own room.

Bobby, who was ten, was just as afraid, but he wouldn't let her give up.

"As long as we're together we'll be okay," he said. "If we go inside crying now, Mom will never let us out again. We've got to be grown up and strong. Come on, we can do it."

And they did. Bobby held her hand all night. And in the morning they strutted triumphantly into the kitchen, closer than ever.

Now, when she needed strength, his words helped her to cope. "Thanks Bobby," she whispered. She chided herself for her anxiety and gathered all her courage. Each time the clock chimed she checked the compass again, until finally, she counted eight bells and Hunt poked his head out.

"Midnight. Everything okay?" he asked.

"Sure, just great," she replied, trying to hide her relief. She felt instantly better now that he was nearby.

"Be out in a second."

He leaned over the satellite navigation receiver then went back to the chart to plot another fix. When he came on deck, he wore a lightweight, red nylon jacket beneath his fluorescent orange safety harness and looked fresh and rested.

"Anything new?" he inquired, scanning the horizon and checking the compass course.

"No, nothing." She sat as though glued to her seat. For a few seconds she had the strange urge to stay with him on deck.

"Okay, see you in three hours then."

She went below to her cabin, but when she stretched out on her bed, sleep wouldn't come. She rolled and tossed trying to get comfortable, but her body seemed too exhausted to relax. When she did start to doze off, every creak of the boat snapped her back to consciousness. All too soon it was her watch again. She dressed and dragged herself back on deck.

Hunt yawned. "Good, there you are. Keep her on the same course. The wind has eased off some but it's still westerly. We had another freighter go by a few minutes ago. You can still see his lights off the stern."

She turned and saw the bright white light behind them.

"See you at six," he said. Then, once again, he set up the self-steering and left her alone.

Within an hour, she had to fight to keep her heavy eyelids from sliding shut. Although she had been unable to sleep in her bed, suddenly now, she was overwhelmingly tired. She tried watching the compass for a while but the slow, smooth swinging of the card beneath the needle was distressingly hypnotic and increased her drowsiness. She crept from the cockpit to the galley, being careful not to wake Hunt, and returned with a box of crackers. Maybe eating would help her stay awake, she thought. She was relieved when the crackers seemed to help. Unfortunately, within minutes of putting down the box, she grew sleepy again, so she was forced to continue eating. Her fearsome demons of the night disappeared, slain by her desperate efforts to remain alert. As the sky lightened in the east, a rosy pink glow decorated the clouds in a brilliant show of color. She stuffed the last crumbs into her mouth and vowed never to eat that brand of crackers again. When Hunt came on watch, she went quickly to her cabin, stripped off her clothes, slipped on a light nightgown, and climbed between the snug sheets. She was asleep in seconds.

When Melissa didn't come on deck at nine o'clock, Hunt waited for ten minutes and then went below. The door to her cabin was wide open. He stopped short without entering. In the morning sunlight streaming through the port, he could clearly see her asleep in her bunk. For a long moment he gave in to the desire to stand and look at her hair cascading across her pillow and her black lashes resting just above the sculptured line of her cheekbone. He memorized the curve of the slightly parted lips that had been tempting him ever since they'd met. Then he silently closed her door and stole back to the cockpit.

He knew the first day at sea was the most difficult for many people. Melissa had surprised him with her fortitude, but when she'd left the cockpit three hours ago she'd looked exhausted. Exhaustion was dangerous on a boat. He decided to let her rest.

His thoughts focused on his attraction to her. And he reminded himself of the lesson he should have learned from what had happened with Myra: don't cross the line from a professional to a personal relationship. He wondered why, at the time, he hadn't foreseen that any involvement would make it impossible for them to continue working together.

Well, one thing's for sure. I'm not going to repeat my mistakes. This time, there won't be any mixing of work and pleasure. There are a lot of other women in the world. I don't need this particular one.

He grasped the wooden steering wheel firmly and concentrated on the only companion he wanted to be involved with, *Whitecap*.

Melissa rushed on deck at ten-fifteen.

"I'm terribly sorry I'm late. I promise it won't happen again. I must have forgotten to set my alarm." Her fingers worked furtively to plait the rumpled strands of hair that she had slung forward over her shoulder.

"No problem, sleeping beauty," he said. "You can owe me one."

"Could I make it up to you by fixing something special for breakfast?"

"No thanks. I've already made myself a peanut butter and jelly sandwich," he replied. "You're not the only one around here who can cook, you know."

Chapter Five

By the third day at sea, Melissa felt more competent in her new role. She read all the instruction manuals in her free time and tried her hand at the helm during spells of moderate weather. She and Hunt began to function as a team and she worked diligently to carry her share of the load. She was eager to comprehend the things he showed her and determined that, in time, she would become a first-class sailor.

In the hours they spent together, she encouraged Hunt to teach her about boating. He seemed to enjoy helping her discover the pleasures of sailing and, now that they were far away from a dock, he acted more cheerful and relaxed. She looked forward to being with him during the six daylight hours when neither of them slept.

One afternoon, he briefed her about the type of charters *Whitecap* provided. "Most of our guests arrive on afternoon flights," he explained. "So the first day all we usually have time to do is leave Red Hook Bay. Caneel Bay and Christmas Cove are both only a short sail away and we can always get to one or the other in daylight. That way the guests can have cocktails and watch the sunset while they get settled in and slow down to island time. Then, you serve a lavish dinner in the cockpit, setting the mood for the rest of the week. You'll have some extra time to prepare that meal so it's the best day to plan anything complex.

"In the morning, you'll want to serve a relatively elaborate breakfast. The first day we tend to get underway late to accommodate any jet lag. I usually take some time to explain the itinerary I've planned and listen to any special requests they might have."

He looked up toward the sails, checked the compass and then continued. "The normal procedure will be to sail to one of the popular tourist spots in the morning and anchor. Our guests may want to go ashore or swim. If they do go ashore, they come back aboard for lunch. Then we weigh anchor and sail to another location. In most cases we'll spend the night there. There's usually one day during the week that we anchor three times. Those are killers. I'll warn you about them so you'll be able to figure your meal plan accordingly. Sometimes, if you're lucky, it works out that they want to eat ashore that night and you won't have to do any quickie meals."

She sat on the edge of her seat listening. She was interested in what her new job would be like. But she was also enjoying the smooth cadence of his voice. "It all sounds pretty hectic, but I'm sure I can manage."

He grinned. "Our job is to give our guests the best vacation they've ever had. And you're an important member of this crew. The quality of the meals is a major consideration in repeat business." He leaned back in his seat. "I do want you to realize, though, that we're a team. The amount of socializing we do with the guests depends entirely on their preferences. Most of the time I like to make myself scarce and give them some privacy. Around mealtime, I'll take care of mixing cocktails and refills. Other than that, I should be available to give you a hand if you need it." A smile played around the corners of his mouth. "You don't want me doing anything too involved in the galley. But I can help you serve, pour wine, brew coffee, things like that."

Melissa almost laughed aloud at the thought of his peanut butter and jelly sandwich for breakfast and the huge mess he'd made for such a simple item. "I'll keep that in mind."

A look of seriousness dimmed the twinkle in his eyes. "While we're talking, there's one more thing I want you to know." He rubbed his chin and loudly inhaled. "You're a very attractive woman, Melissa, and I strongly suggest that any time there's anyone other than just the two of us aboard, you sleep with your door locked."

Melissa drew back in surprise, then remembered that twice in the last few days she'd left her door, not only unlocked, but wide open.

He adjusted his hat and looked around. She had the feeling he was avoiding her eyes. "And if anyone makes any unwanted advances, let me know. I'll straighten him out."

Melissa felt her chin start to rise. "I'm sure I can do that for myself if necessary." It was a prideful thing to say and she knew it. She always felt terribly threatened when any man was overly aggressive.

"Well, maybe, but you never know. It's not that I don't think you can handle yourself. It's just that some guys won't lay off unless they think the lady is already taken."

It took Melissa a minute to realize what he was suggesting. That he would lead a bothersome man to believe they were involved. She was annoyed at first but took comfort in his offer of protection. For a fleeting second she even pictured the two of them as a couple. She shook off the tantalizing image. *Actually, I could take all this as a strange kind of compliment, except that he's made it quite clear that he isn't interested in me.*

She felt compelled to say something. "I guess I'll keep that in mind, too," she finally responded. Then she stretched out in the sun and closed her eyes.

* * *

Huge, cold raindrops splattering on her face woke Melissa at almost the same moment as the sound of Hunt's voice.

"You'd better get back in the cockpit, Melissa. We've got a squall coming."

Suddenly, the wind lashed the boat with a vicious gust. She felt the deck slant steeply beneath her. She grabbed a rail and hung on tight. The wind started to howl through the rigging. The water all around them was whipped into confused white foam.

Hunt sprang into action. He released the jib sheet. The big genoa foresail snapped in the wind like a bull-whip. Melissa struggled to climb into the cockpit. White water continued to roar past the hull. Hunt furled the genoa.

"Make sure your safety harness is hooked on," he yelled.

Her heart raced. Her knuckles turned white grasping a nearby winch. Wind-driven raindrops stung her face. The boat heeled precariously in another strong gust. She braced her feet. She felt herself sliding. Then suddenly, nothing. As quickly as they started, the storm winds were gone. She stared in awe as a line of froth marched away from the boat.

"Melissa, quick! Take the wheel."

Hunt pulled his shirt off as she scurried to obey his command. He rushed past her, kicking off his shoes. In seconds, he was at the bow. She lost sight of him in an opaque white curtain of moisture. Then, the raindrops grew smaller. He reappeared with a mop in his hand. She laughed and her grip on the wheel relaxed.

She watched Hunt work. Starting at the bow, he used the mop to direct water into every corner and onto every fitting, washing away the coating of salt crystals that the ocean spray had deposited over the last few days. His shorts were wet through, and the water poured off his tanned, muscular back. But he seemed unconcerned. His expression was so happy that she thought he might burst into a song.

Melissa found it difficult to keep her attention on the compass course. He looked so vital and masculine that she wanted to study his every move. But she was glad he was so engrossed in his task and wasn't watching her steer.

The wind was sort of off to the right, she rationalized, so she should steer a little bit that way, until the sail started to luff. She turned the wheel a quarter turn. The edge of the sail started to flutter. *Too far.*

She bit her lip and turned back a little to the left. She read the compass. *Okay, hold it there.*

The wind tangled loose strands of her wet hair and blew it into her face. She pushed it behind her ear and wiped the drops of rainwater from her eyelashes.

She looked up at Hunt, worried that he might see her lack of finesse. But he was busy, whistling as he cleaned his way toward the stern.

When the rain stopped, Hunt completed a stroke with the mop and stood. Then, with a broad smile, he slipped back into the cockpit.

Melissa looked up at his face and chuckled. Water was running into his eyes and dripping off his chin. She reached out and gently pushed his rain-softened hair to one side of his forehead. Immediately, the intimacy of the gesture registered in her mind. She felt her face heat up and flush crimson.

His eyes questioned hers for half a second. She quickly looked down toward the deck and handed him his shirt. As he wrung out the shirt and used it to wipe his face, the sun broke out from behind the clouds of the fast-moving squall. Prisms of light reflected from the jewel-like raindrops beaded on the wet boat.

"She sure looks beautiful again, doesn't she?" he asked.

Early on the morning of the eighth day, Hunt came into the cockpit and announced they would be sighting land soon. Within an hour, Melissa spotted a dull, gray smudge on the horizon that grew steadily larger, then several more mounds appeared on each side. For a while, the lumps of land seemed to be a mirage floating in the air just above the surface of the sea, but gradually they took shape behind the waves. As she watched, the grays became colors and the colors separated and brightened. Steep green hills dotted with miniature buildings came into focus. For one fleeting moment she felt a tinge of sadness thinking that her adventure was almost over. Quickly, the thrill of the landfall wiped it from her mind.

Even though it wasn't her watch, she stayed in the

cockpit all morning, staring at the islands as the boat sailed past. She knew that they had reached their destination and the trip was over. But one thought kept recurring in her mind. *This isn't an ending, it's a new beginning.*

Chapter Six

Melissa felt like jumping up and down and clapping her hands in excitement. It was just like Hunt had said it would be. Red Hook Harbor on the eastern end of the island of St. Thomas was bursting with a fleet of dazzling charter boats. He'd told her that from there the yachts whisked their sun-worshiping passengers to exotic, picturesque anchorages, deposited them over coral reefs, and wined and dined them in opulent luxury. Her books had said the yachts that arrived in Red Hook and in Caneel Bay, on St. John, were some of the most expensive and beautiful in the world. As soon as she saw the bay, she understood that here *Whitecap* was amongst her kind.

From the welcome Hunt received, she could tell that he was well known to the other crews. As they wove

61

their way through the fleet of boats in the harbor, he waved and returned the greetings of old friends and shouted jovial warnings to competitors.

Melissa stared wide-eyed at the big yachts. She hadn't expected this many boats. She watched the activity of tenders streaking back and forth to shore, tourists crowding the waterfront, and the inter-island ferry depositing its load of cars and passengers on the battered dock. The chanting of street vendors and the reggae music emanating from the restaurants and shops threatened to overwhelm her sea-calmed sensibilities. But, at the same time, she was thrilled.

"It's all so *fantastic*," she told Hunt as he tied the bow to a bobbing mooring ball near the wharf.

For the first time in eight days *Whitecap* came to rest.

Hunt stood, turned toward Melissa and smiled. "It's always great. Even after all the times I've seen it. But would you tear yourself away for a second and make a note of the time we arrived? I can enter it into the ship's log later."

For nearly two hours, Melissa helped Hunt with a routine of cleanup and inspection. She learned how to coil lines and put up the sun awning. Later, after they finished checking the engine and washing down the teak decks, she brought him a tall glass of ice-cold tea on the aft deck and placed two thick steaks on the barbecue grill.

"Well, Melissa, tomorrow the real work begins. But for tonight we're still free. What do you say after dinner we clean ourselves up and go ashore? There's a place called Langley's near the waterfront where something interesting is always going on. It's the local hangout. You can meet some of the other charter crews."

"Sounds great," she said, then joked, "Nothing personal, but I could use a little social contact with the rest of the world."

"And I always thought of myself as a fascinating conversationalist," he quipped with his chin out and his hand spread wide over his heart. "I am truly cut to the quick."

They both laughed.

They ate the tender, honey-basted steaks, a crisp cabbage salad, and brown, crusty rolls still warm from the oven, with a hunger induced by the sea. Then Hunt warned her, "Be ready in an hour, woman, or I'll go ashore without you."

Melissa took a long, refreshing shower. She shook out her tightly woven braids and shampooed the last of the salt from her hair. Then she dried herself and spread cool, soothing lotion on her sun-parched skin. Looking in the mirror, she appraised her new, golden tan and decided to wear the white sundress she'd purchased the day before leaving Wilmington. A pair of large, Chinese red earrings added just the right touch. She swept her clean, shiny hair to one side and draped it forward onto her shoulder. Satisfied with her reflection, she slipped into a pair of matching red sandals. But then she glanced at the hard soles, thought about the woodwork, and slipped them back off. She decided to carry them until she got ashore. Ready at last, she went on deck to wait for Hunt.

As she came into the cockpit a low wolf whistle pierced the quiet. "You look fantastic. A little over-dressed for Langley's, but fantastic."

She silently admired his rugged, clean-scrubbed look. He wore neatly pressed shorts and an open-necked, white polo shirt. Slight dampness weighed down and tamed his normally windblown hair.

"All ashore that's goin' ashore," he mimicked the navy command as he helped her climb down into the inflatable tender.

He gave her a short lesson in how to start the out-board motor, and then they were off, speeding the short distance toward solid land.

She laughed at her first steps on the dock. "I know I'm ashore, but I still feel like I'm rocking."

He smiled. "You'll adjust in a little while. Think of it as being land-sick."

They walked into Langley's together and several people eagerly greeted Hunt. He introduced Melissa to everyone at once, making it almost impossible for her to remember who each person was. She struggled to associate names with faces, looking for memory de-vices to ease her task. Soon, they were seated around a large table with three other charter crews, sipping various tropical fruit drinks, some of which contained a liberal portion of the locally distilled rum.

Melissa ordered passion fruit juice, and she studied

the restaurant while enjoying the sweet, pulpy beverage. Langley's occupied a small, square building one block off the main street. Outside, she had smiled at the gaudy blue paint that had been splashed liberally over the weathered shingles, and the vivid yellow shutters that creaked constantly as they swayed slightly in the breeze. Inside, she saw the same blue paint coating the walls between large, unscreened windows. A scarred, wooden bar with several rickety-looking stools stretched along one wall. The opposite wall was papered with colorful photographs of charter boats. Several tables with plain, red tablecloths and ornate, brass lanterns clustered around a small dance floor. According to Hunt, a poetry-reciting waiter served spicy, local foods to those daring enough to sample the cuisine.

As people came and went, Melissa discovered that the crews that gathered here formed a small close-knit community. Nevertheless, they were a diverse group. She met everyone from career captains with years of experience at sea to ex-executive dropouts, floating around taking jobs as deckhands or shipwrights. Several boat crews were husband-and-wife teams. Some crews owned their boats; others, like Hunt, worked for absentee owners.

As she listened, they swapped news and information and talked about boats and people they all seemed to know. She learned that the former crew of *Hushabye* had opened a restaurant in St. Croix, that *Ragtime* needed a cook, that Sarah on *Skimmer* had taught high school history for ten years, and that Trinidad had good prices on anti-fouling bottom paint.

Around eight-thirty, a new couple arrived and rushed over to greet Hunt. The tall, striking blond embraced him warmly and kissed him passionately on the lips. He returned her kiss and, picking her up in his embrace, swung her in a full circle. Their companions around the table hooted and applauded the display. When she was firmly settled back on the floor, the man with her shook Hunt's hand vigorously and clapped him on the back. He had dark, wavy hair and dark eyes and a tawny complexion that accentuated his narrow chin. His arms were tanned and muscular, and he exuded a purely animal-like magnetism that sharply contrasted with Hunt's wholesomeness.

"It's about time you got here," he told Hunt.

The blond, meanwhile, was standing on tiptoes, scanning the room. She turned back to Hunt and threaded her arm around his. "Where's Myra? I don't see her."

Hunt's smile dimmed. "She's gone, Liz. Quit over the summer."

Liz's eyes widened. "Gone? But I thought you two were, well, getting along, so to speak."

"The arrangement sort of fell apart, and she found a better prospect." His voice was matter-of-fact, but Melissa saw turbulent emotion in his eyes.

"Anyway, *Whitecap*'s got a new galley slave now." He looked directly at Melissa. "Melissa, this is Liz. She's won the charter fleet's cooking contest for three years running. So steal any recipes you can, and tell her no secrets."

Laughter rang in Melissa's ears as she and Liz exchanged greetings. Then everyone resumed their rowdy conversations.

Melissa sat silently with her eyes focused on Hunt. He was talking with Liz and her companion, Erich, and flashing his charming, boyish smile. Since their arrival Melissa had noticed that Hunt was very popular with the female members of the group. *And why not?* She studied his face for a moment, noticing the tiny wrinkles next to his eyes, a product of his infectious grin. His tousled, sun-bleached hair was only a shade darker than the golden hair of his eyebrows. His face was rugged, yet handsome and was in perfect harmony with his wide shoulders, trim hips and muscular legs. *He has the kind of looks women are attracted to. Even I've got to admit that I find him appealing.*

She turned her thoughts to the remark Liz had made about Myra. Hunt had been obviously disturbed. Melissa absently swirled the ice and juice in her glass. *I wonder what really caused the last cook on* Whitecap *to quit?*

A decrease in the number of voices around her drew her thoughts back to Langley's. Hunt had his arm snugly around Liz, and they were walking slowly away from the table, talking too quietly for her to hear their words. An uncomfortable feeling came over Melissa seeing them together so close. She could only identify it as jealousy. She sat up stiffly in her chair.

I'm being silly. I can't expect him to hang around just me. We've been together for eight days. Now he's here with his friends. Of course he's going to circulate and catch up on what's been happening in their lives. For heaven's sake, it's not like we're involved. I certainly don't want to get clingy. I just need to meet some other people so that I don't start depending solely on Hunt for company.

She tore her eyes away from Hunt and turned to the woman next to her. "So, which boat did you say you're on?"

She didn't see Hunt again until an hour later, when the occupants of another table prepared to leave. "Hey, Hunt. Want to throw some darts?" one of them shouted.

"Nah, maybe next time," he called back from across the room and waved.

At ten, a three-piece band arrived and began blasting out rhythmic but mediocre music. Hunt had been circulating from table to table. Melissa was lost in her thoughts, and feeling lonely in the crowded room. She stared down at her crossed fingers and didn't look up when he walked to her table and sat down.

"A penny for your thoughts," he offered.

She raised her moist eyes.

"I was just thinking of someone I loved very much who died recently," she whispered so low that he leaned closer to hear her.

He reached across the table and covered her hand with his. "Still hurts pretty bad, I take it."

His touch was warm and comforting. She sniffled, then straightened her shoulders. "Bad, but better." Reluctantly, she removed one hand from under his and wiped away a tear. "I was just thinking about something he said a few months ago, that one drop of love was more powerful than any disease, that with a little bit of love a person could conquer anything. I guess he was wrong, though. In the end it didn't matter whether I loved him or not, his disease won."

She looked at Hunt's perplexed expression and wondered if he had ever been devastated by the loss of love. "It's strange what you remember about people, isn't it? I guess all this must sound kind of silly to you."

"No, not at all," he told her. Then he jerked his head toward the dance floor and smiled. "Come on, you're not allowed to be depressed. We're supposed to party tonight, remember? Let's dance."

She looked into his sympathetic eyes and tried to forget her gloom. "I guess if you can take it, I can."

He laughed and stood up and began moving his body in time with the fifties beat booming from the bandstand. His version of the twist was outrageous, and she burst out laughing at his antics. In no time, she was breathless from trying to match his efforts. She was secretly relieved when the band ended their extended rendition of the dance tune and transitioned to a slow ballad. Without hesitation he smiled and opened his arms to her. She accepted his invitation, bringing her body close to his and resting her forehead comfortably on his chin.

Slowly moving to the intoxicating music, Melissa felt content. The faint scent of his aftershave blended with the salt air. A lazy fan whirled over their heads, cooling her. He steered her around the dance floor skillfully. Her legs grew attuned to his graceful movements, and responsively, instinctively she followed his lead. Gently, he entwined his fingers in her hair and held her head to him. She closed her eyes and sighed. It felt so natural, so right, to be enjoying his embrace.

Suddenly, she stiffened. They were dancing far too close for friends. And she'd let herself get too attracted for comfort. Her defenses shifted into high gear, and she widened the gap between them. "Sorry if I've been a drag on you tonight."

"What do you mean?"

"I mean, I appreciate your introducing me to everybody. But you don't have to feel obligated to dance with me."

"There's no obligation felt."

"I hope not. Because, you know, I can take care of myself. If you wanted to go off with Liz or something, I mean." As the words slipped out, she regretted them. Even to her own ears she sounded like she was trying to send him away.

He released her from his embrace. "I'll tell you what. You take the tender and go back to the boat whenever you're good and ready. I'm going to go throw a few darts."

Melissa felt the blood rising in her face. "That's fine with me."

His eyes burned into hers for a minute then he turned away, heading toward the door.

"Strange fella, our Hunt," Erich said.

Melissa bit her lip as he stepped beside her. She wondered how many others had witnessed her exchange with Hunt in the middle of the dance floor.

"If I had you in my arms, I certainly wouldn't rush off. May I fill in for him?"

She remembered his arrival, earlier in the evening. "Are you and Liz . . . ?"

"No, nothing of the sort. We crew on the same boat, that's all." He held out his arms. "Shall we?"

She shrugged and went to him, and he politely held her waist at arms' length. Slowly, she calmed down and began to enjoy his company. Soon she was laughing at his endless supply of anecdotes.

When they sat to rest, he talked about the islands. "One of the things I like most is how close the stars appear. Sometimes it seems you could almost reach out and touch them."

"They are wonderful," Melissa agreed. "Sailing down here, seeing the stars was the best part of standing watches at night."

"There are a lot of shooting stars this time of year, as well as the constellations to look for. Some night you should come out to *Crystal Lady* with me and watch them for awhile."

"Definitely not tonight," Melissa said. "I'm still tired from standing watches."

"Oh, yes. I'd forgotten about that. Have you seen the island at all?"

"No, I've never been here before."

"Well, in that case I insist that you let me give you the grand tour. How about tomorrow night? We can go into Charlotte Amalie and you can see some of the city. Then we can have dinner. I know a really fantastic Greek restaurant."

Melissa was anxious to see St. Thomas. She knew she would enjoy sightseeing more if she had company than she would if she went alone. "That sounds like fun."

They danced again. But at midnight Melissa had to sit down. Her body was still on the ship's routine, and she was exhausted.

As she was leaving Erich said, "I just remembered, I have to be in town all afternoon tomorrow. Would you mind if we meet at the street market? About six o'clock?"

"I'll be there," Melissa promised. Then she said goodnight and stepped out into the cool night air.

"Ready to go?"

Melissa jumped. Hunt was leaning against the outside wall, his hands stuffed in his shorts pockets and his legs crossed at the ankles.

"Why, yes. I am." She smiled, amused at her fright but pleased to see him there.

He walked to her side and indicated that she should

walk in front of him with a sweep of his hand. "I decided making sure a lady isn't alone on the streets at night is more important than darts."

The next morning, Hunt was businesslike and rather formal. Melissa missed his pleasant banter but returned his coolness and very carefully avoided any mention of the night before.

As morning turned to afternoon, they each made several trips to shore ordering supplies and provisions.

Melissa stopped at a phone booth on one of her trips and called Morgan. "We made it here safely," she told him.

"Well, I'm certainly relieved to hear that. I've been worried sick."

She chuckled. "It was marvelous, Morgan. You should see how beautiful the nights are far from the lights of land. The stars twinkle right down to the horizon. And we saw porpoises and flying fish during the day."

She stuck one finger into her uncovered ear to block out the noise of a passing truck. Through the roar she heard him ask, "Will you write me and tell me all about it?"

"Yes. I won't be able to call too often because the rates are terribly expensive."

"I'll look forward to your letters."

Melissa hung up and went back to *Whitecap*. Just after four o'clock, she brought up the subject she could no longer avoid.

"I'm planning to go ashore for dinner tonight," she announced to Hunt, careful to keep her voice as impersonal as she could. She didn't want to sound as if she were asking his permission. After all, when no guests were aboard, her evenings were supposed to be free. She tried to ignore the disturbing feeling that she would have preferred Hunt be the one to show her the town.

She saw rampant curiosity on his face. But he said, "Fine. I was planning on going in myself."

Melissa escaped to her cabin to dress. She showered, then put on a denim skirt and a sleeveless, cotton blouse. She pulled her hair back and twisted it into a tight coil. Critically, she looked in her mirror and ran her eyes over the prim, Peter Pan collar and conservative hemline. Her reflection brought her to attention. *I've just put on the least attractive outfit I own for a date with Erich.*

When she opened her jewelry box to choose her earrings, her eyes fell to a gold fraternity pin sitting securely in one corner. She picked it up. Memories flooded back of Randy, her college sweetheart, her first love. It still hurt to remember the day that he'd surprised and humiliated her with the announcement that he was marrying someone else.

She thought about how, all of her life, love had led to pain. Her mother had died when she was ten, her older brother had been killed in a skydiving accident, she'd lost Randy, and now, Mr. Barnes. The pin reminded her to stay aloof, stay cool. She'd let down her guard with Mr. Barnes, but she wouldn't let it happen again.

She told herself she was safe dating Erich. *My attraction to Hunt is the danger.*

Melissa placed the pin carefully back in the jewelry box and put on a pair of gold loop earrings. A veil of sadness seemed to weigh her down, and she considered staying aboard tonight. She sighed. It would be silly to hide in her cabin in a tropical paradise like this. She had a life to live, she had to get out and experience the island. Pulling herself to her feet, she finished dressing, even though she had no enthusiasm for the evening to come.

When they reached the shore, Hunt appeared surprised at her announcement: "You can have the tender to get back to the boat tonight. I've made other arrangements."

She saw curiosity in his eyes, or was it hurt? But he only nodded. She started off toward the bus stop feeling uneasy about leaving him there alone.

She sighed and flagged down the approaching bus. *He said he had plans. A man with looks like his probably won't be alone for long. So why does that depress me even more?*

Chapter Seven

The street market was empty at this time of day, except for two chattering women sweeping up debris near a scarred old table. Melissa spotted Erich immediately.

"You look absolutely gorgeous," he said. "I will have every man in town envying me for being your escort."

Melissa felt her face flush with embarrassment at his exaggerated compliment.

"Shall we walk for a while?" he asked. "That way I can show you some places of interest, and show you off to a lot of people."

He explained that all the duty-free shops were already closed and that the tourists who usually pack the streets eager for duty-free bargains had returned to their cruise ships or hotels with their treasures. As he talked, they strolled along the narrow streets and intersecting alleyways, window-shopping and pretending to find fault with the exquisite jewelry and expensive perfumes.

The town was a unique combination of very old and very new that surprised Melissa at every corner. At one street sign, they laughed as she tied her tongue in knots trying to pronounce the long, Danish name. At the next, the golden arches of a McDonald's fast-food restaurant accentuated the more recent American cultural invasion. After they wandered through the shopping district, they walked past Fort Christian and Erich told her a version of its history that she suspected was slanted by his pride in his German ancestry.

"There's a place called Blackbeard's Seat you should see also," he told her. "But it's better in the daylight, when you can see the various colors of the steps. Let's go by and look at the architecture of Government House, and then go to dinner."

She agreed and they trudged up the steep hill and past the government office buildings. Then they climbed a narrow stairway to a cozy Greek restaurant hidden away in the center of the city.

The owner seemed to know Erich well, and seated them at a small table for two in a quiet corner on the stone terrace. Melissa was thrilled by the bird's-eye view. She watched twinkling points of light scatter over the city below as twilight enveloped the island.

Melissa caught her breath. *It's so magical. I wonder if Hunt has ever seen this sight. He'd appreciate it. It's like the beauty of a glittering ocean.*

"Let me order for you," Erich suggested. "There are several dishes you must sample here, and I couldn't forgive myself if you didn't taste them all."

Melissa savored the wonderful aromas in the room. "That's probably best. I'm smelling so many tempting ingredients, I don't think I can choose."

After the waiter left, Erich asked, "Have you been crewing long?"

"Actually, no. This is my first job on a boat." She remembered her interview with Hunt for a few seconds, then continued, "What about you?"

Erich laughed. "I was born on a boat. Not *Crystal Lady*, of course. My parents had sailed to Miami to deliver a load of pineapples from the Bahamas. I came along a month ahead of schedule. I was born on a small American vessel anchored in the harbor that just happened to have a doctor on board."

"And that's how you came to be a German who's also an American citizen?"

"Yes. Years later my parents left the Bahamas for these islands, and I've been here ever since."

"Are they still on a boat here?"

"No. They disappeared in a storm on their way back from Venezuela when I was sixteen. That's when I started to fend for myself."

"I'm sorry," Melissa said softly. "I know how painful it is to lose a parent; losing both at once must be devastating. Let's talk about more cheerful things. How long have you been working on *Crystal Lady*?"

"Too long." He chuckled. "I should be moving on. I'm just waiting for the right opportunity to come along."

Their food arrived, beginning with a meze platter of small fried cheese pies and stuffed grape leaves. It was as delicious as Erich had promised. Then they were served a main course of marinated chicken with tiny onions and vinegar and a pilaf with green lentils. Melissa savored the various flavors, trying to guess what spices had been used to achieve each special taste. By the time their dessert of poached fruit arrived, she was convinced the chef was an absolute genius. They ate until she felt she would burst. Then she sent a note back to the kitchen complimenting the chef on his efforts.

Afterward, they strolled leisurely back through town and along Waterfront Drive, then took a taxi back to Red Hook Bay. Erich took Melissa's hand and helped her into his tender.

A few minutes later he brought the tender up to *Crystal Lady*'s stern.

"I don't think I should come aboard," Melissa told him.

"The night is still young. The view of the stars from the forward deck is very romantic."

"I'm sorry if I gave you the wrong idea, Erich. I want us to be friends."

He leaned close to her and his eyes focused on her

lips. She felt his hand brush a stray strand of hair from her temple, then his finger trace the line of her jaw. He bent to kiss her.

Melissa turned her head moving her mouth away from his. *I should have seen this coming.* "I think I'd better go," she stammered.

He whispered close to her ear, "You don't want to leave me now, darling. The best part of the evening is just beginning."

Melissa twisted away from him. "I've already had a very nice evening, Erich. Now, I want to go home."

"We could do splendid things together," he said softly.

He was obviously quite aware of his physical attractiveness and she was sure that she was not the first woman to be invited aboard *Crystal Lady* to "see the stars."

"You're presuming way too much, Erich. I'm not in the least bit interested in that kind of relationship."

He retreated a little, speaking slowly and studying her face. "Well, not tonight maybe. But one day, you'll change your mind."

Melissa shook her head. "Don't count on it. Now please take me back to *Whitecap*."

Earlier in the evening when Hunt had figured out who, besides Melissa, was missing from the crowd at Langley's, he'd slammed his glass onto the table. *Erich! Of course! The man is famous for his conquests.* Since then, his mood had grown somber and the jokes circulating through the crowd had seemed humorless. He'd stayed, trying to join in the friendly discussions, but he couldn't concentrate on the banter.

At eleven o'clock he took another walk past the dock, as he had been doing at fifteen-minute intervals all night long. Again, he looked for Erich's tender. But this time, it was gone.

Hunt climbed into *Whitecap*'s tender and uncleated the dock line. As he did, he attempted to sort out his feelings. *Knock it off, buddy*, he told himself. *It could never work and you know it. She's the kind of woman who grew up dreaming of a husband who works a respectable nine-to-five job, at least four kids, a big house in the suburbs, two cars in the garage and the security of money in the bank. You don't even own your own boat. And what makes you think she'd want to live with you even if you did?*

He took a deep breath, started the outboard, and slowly idled back toward *Whitecap*. But halfway there, he decided to take a detour and made a loop around the harbor so that he would pass *Crystal Lady* on the way.

Erich's tender was tied to the stern. A dim light glowed belowdecks in the area where Hunt knew Erich's cabin was located.

Hunt's shoulders sagged in despair and he shifted the outboard to neutral. *Will Melissa think I'm insane if I knock on the hull and demand she leave Erich? Is there anything I can do to get her away from him and keep her safe?*

He tore his eyes away from the light and stared down the length of the bay, shivering from a sudden bone-penetrating chill that was inconsistent with the warm night air. Red and green channel marker lights blinked slowly in the distance. His eyes absently followed the running lights on a motoryacht aiming into the blackness past the island of St. John. His gaze slid to where *Whitecap* was moored. A light flickered. He narrowed his eyes. *What? Is she being burglarized?*

He jammed the throttle to full and sped back toward his own boat. He killed the motor to glide the last few yards in silence, then removed his shoes and crept aboard barefooted. As he moved through the cockpit, he grabbed a heavy winch handle. Holding it like a club, he tiptoed down the companionway to confront the intruder. He saw a bright stream of light spilling from the crack of Melissa's door.

He's going through her stuff!

His sweaty hand squeezed the weapon tighter. He drew back his foot and kicked the door open.

Melissa screamed. Her hand flew up to her throat. A hairbrush flew into the air and crashed to the floor. "Oh, Hunt! What in the world . . . ?"

"Are you okay?"

"Yes. Why? What's happened?"

"Well . . . ah . . . nothing I guess. I mean, I thought there was a burglar. Forget it. My mistake." His eyes took in the shapely figure beneath her thin nightgown. He caught his breath and fought down the urge to sweep her into his arms. "Sorry I barged in on you, but I thought you were . . . were you with Erich tonight?"

She jumped up from her bed, grabbed a robe from her closet, put it on, and spun to face him. "Yes. Why? Has something happened? Was *Crystal Lady* burglarized?"

He tried to regroup his emotions and assume a businesslike manner. "No. There isn't any burglar, just a mix-up."

She glanced toward the winch handle still clutched in his hand.

He slid the hand holding his weapon behind his back. "Liz told me last night that she's quitting as his cook. That means he'll be looking to hire a new one. He'll probably try to steal someone from another boat."

"Do you mean 'steal' as in burglarize *Whitecap* and carry me off?"

"No, as in offer you more money to take the job."

"He never even mentioned it."

"I'm relieved to hear that. The man always seems to mean trouble. I thought that maybe he was trying to pull something underhanded. Personally, I feel it's a good idea to try to keep away from him whenever possible."

He saw her posture stiffen. "Am I supposed to be grateful for your concern? Or should I thank you for trying to tell me who to associate with? At least he doesn't storm around at night kicking doors in and scaring people half to death."

He took a step toward her. "I just don't want to lose you," he said, thinking that he was concerned about more than losing a cook.

"Well, you don't have to worry. I don't think he was looking for a cook tonight."

He frowned. *If I know Erich, that's probably very true. But he didn't get what he was looking for. She's here instead of being with him.*

Hunt decided not to pursue the subject any farther. He had no right to pry into her personal life any more than he already had. "Good, see you in the morning then." He turned and, suddenly feeling better than he had all night, began whistling as he went to his cabin.

Whitecap began her ninth season as a charter yacht three days later. But her age certainly didn't show. She was spotless. And, because she had always been impeccably maintained, she looked as beautiful to Hunt as the day he'd first seen her. The supplies and provisions were stored away in cupboards and lockers. The freezer was filled with exotic delicacies. Hunt felt bright and crisp in the new uniforms Roger had sent. Everything was in readiness for another season of trade wind enjoyment.

Hunt went ashore to meet their charter guests. He stopped at the post office, as usual. When he picked up the mail he noticed an envelope addressed to Melissa and puzzled over the return addressee: Morgan Black. *Why does that name sound familiar?* Then he shrugged his shoulders, checked his watch, and ran to flag down a cab.

He was at the airport at eleven. But the plane was delayed so, while he waited, he phoned Roger.

"Any news?" he asked.

"A little, but nothing you want to hear," Roger said. "The legal battle still rages. But, if the will stands, *Whitecap* is definitely on the block. The new owner doesn't think your baby is profitable enough. Last year's loss is probably a big factor in that."

"But we both know that's not true, Rog. This season is going to make up for last year, and then some. Can't you reason with them?"

"I've tried. I've also been trying to get them to listen to your plan for taking her to Greece and Turkey for the summers. But so far, I've been put off. There are just too many lawyers involved. Sorry, but it looks like your days are numbered. Unless, of course, you buy her."

"Not much chance of that."

"Why not? I thought you had some kind of a trust fund from your grandfather. Can't you tap into part of that?"

Hunt fisted his hand at the mention of the trust. "It's possible, but I can't touch it on my own for another two years. My father is temporary trustee. He would have to agree to any early release of the funds. I think you know what that means."

"Yeah, I remember. He doesn't consider chartering a worthwhile business," Roger said. "I guess you're between a rock and a hard place, buddy. But if you want *Whitecap* bad enough, maybe your new plan would convince him."

Hunt gave a sour laugh. "Buying a boat was never high on his list of preferred investments. It's no use, Rog. As much as I hate the thought, *Whitecap* will be sold long before I could persuade him to release the money."

After Hunt hung up the phone, he did the calculations in his head once more. He knew the dollar value of the boat from the latest insurance survey. There was no way. He had saved for years, planning that someday he'd be able to make a deal with Mr. Barnes, and *Whitecap* would be his. But even if he put every penny he had into her and went into hock up to his eyebrows, he probably still couldn't manage to buy *Whitecap* for at least two years. He had the fleeting thought that maybe Roger was right. Maybe *Whitecap* was worth making the effort of asking for what was his, no matter how futile that effort might be. *No, I won't do that. Dad just doesn't understand a business that doesn't have land or buildings or machines.*

Frustrated, he banged his fist into the concrete wall next to the telephone. He winced as a sharp pain seared his wrist and radiated up his arm. For a moment, he thought he might have broken his hand. Methodically, he bent each finger in turn to check that they still functioned. He walked away in pain. But even that physical ache couldn't overshadow the haunting knowledge that *Whitecap* was indeed for sale.

The arrival announcement for flight 436 echoed through the terminal. Forcing his most charming smile to mask his distress, he collected the couple who were paying for a week of fun, sunshine and pampering. He gave them a brief tour of the island and then loaded their luggage into *Whitecap*'s tender. As they crossed the bay to the waiting sailboat, a lump formed in his throat at the sight of *Whitecap*. She was the one thing in his life that he cared for without reservation. *How much longer will I be her captain? And what will happen to her after she's sold?*

Chapter Eight

The next few days went by in a blur. Hunt and Melissa worked from dawn until way past dusk, tending to the comforts of the charter guests. On the last morning of the charter, he took the guests ashore so they could explore the ruins of a rum distillery. After he returned to *Whitecap*, he wandered into the galley where Melissa was involved in preparations for lunch.

"Mark and Ashley are ashore. I'll go back and pick them up in an hour," he told her.

She nodded. "Good. That gives me plenty of time."

"What are you up to?"

"Experimenting with a fruit salad. The papaya needed a little sweetening so I poached it in a pineapple and honey syrup. I'm figuring on cubed mango, sliced carambola, and some kiwi for texture and color diversity. Maybe I'll garnish with a halved straw-berry."

"Sounds delicious." He lifted the cover off a pot on the stove and inhaled deeply of the mouth-watering aroma. "Callaloo soup?"

"It's a surprise for Mark. When he first came aboard, he mentioned that he had it once a few years ago in Martinique and has been dying for more ever since. I'm just letting it simmer. It's ready except for the crabmeat."

"Both Mark and Ashley are crazy about you, you know."

"They're nice people. It's not like I'm working at all when I'm doing things for them."

"It always helps when you hit it off with the guests." He listened to her humming as she peeled a ripe mango. "And the fact that you're having a good time is contagious."

She smiled and looked apologetic. "I've been trying not to get too carried away."

Hunt laughed. "I couldn't tell." She started to blush and he felt a stab of regret for poking fun at her en-thusiasm. "Hey, don't be embarrassed about it. It's great. You're so bubbly and cheerful that even Scrooge would have to enjoy himself."

He thought about how much fun he'd had in the last week, watching her thrill to the sights and places that he never tired of visiting. She'd been like a kid on Christmas morning. It was refreshing to see her una-bashed pleasure.

She pushed the mango peels into a rough pile and picked up another fruit. "Well, still, I should try to be more professional in the future."

"Don't worry about it. You shouldn't have to change just to please somebody else. Smell the flowers, gasp at the sunsets, go ahead and dance a jig on the deck if you feel like it. This is paradise."

Melissa looked thoughtful for a few seconds. "I have been really happy here, haven't I? Isn't that strange?"

"Strange? Why?"

"It's just that I haven't felt like this in a long time." She gave a little laugh, shook her head, and he saw her make an exaggerated effort to appear engrossed in separating the mango seed from the pulp. "Never mind."

He sat quietly and watched her slim fingers at work. His thoughts went back to their conversation at Langley's about the loss of someone she'd loved. Was it that loss that was causing her to look so sad and thoughtful?

Silently, he encouraged her to make the most of life. *Don't change just to please somebody else. You're great just the way you are.*

Two weeks later, the guests were a husband and wife and their nine-year-old son. During dinner on the second night, Hunt helped Melissa clear away the appetizer plates. He paused in the galley as he passed through, scooped a little salsa from the dip bowl with the last fried plantain round, and popped it into his mouth.

"Mmmm. Perfect plantains. What's next?"

"Sliced chicken breast with passionfruit sauce. There's banana flambé for dessert."

"Little Jamie ought to like that."

She smiled, letting her playful intent show. "I thought he might."

Back at the cockpit table, Melissa served the entrée and Hunt conversed with the guests.

Over the last couple weeks, she had discovered that Hunt was the perfect captain and host. When Roger booked the charters, he had each guest fill out a questionnaire to help Hunt plan their itinerary. But Hunt understood that people didn't always put their true desires on paper. He wanted the guests to enjoy sailing, and it showed in his actions.

"If you want to change our itinerary at any time," Hunt told them, "feel free. I know it's hard to plan everything out in advance, especially if you've never been here before. You never know what might catch your interest."

Jamie spoke up. "Can we go shark fishing? And catch a really big one so that I can have one of his teeth?"

Hunt chuckled. "We can do some fishing, but I can't guarantee what you'll catch. Usually, we don't try to attract sharks to the islands we visit. You wouldn't want them hanging around while you're swimming, would you?"

Jamie shrugged his shoulders and wrinkled his nose. "I guess not. But if they did come, I could use my dad's dive knife and scare them away."

"Tell you what," Hunt said. "There's a resort on Virgin Gorda that has a big shark tank near the dock. If it's okay with your folks, we could go out there if you want to. You can stand right next to the tank and see the sharks up close. You can even watch the groundskeeper feeding them. And I happen to know a fisherman on the island who has a collection of hundreds of shark's teeth. I can take you over to visit with him. We're old friends and I'm sure he'll have a couple he can part with."

Jamie turned to his mother and father. "Could we do that?"

His father answered. "I don't see why not. As a matter of fact I'd be interested in that myself. Let's go there instead of Jost Van Dyke." He turned toward his wife and she nodded.

"Sounds like a great plan," Hunt said. He turned toward Jamie and continued. "We can put a line out and troll on our way through Sir Francis Drake Channel. Maybe we'll catch a huge barracuda. They're just as scary and twice as much fun to catch as sharks."

"If we get one, I want to have my picture taken holding it, so I can show it to all my friends when we get home," Jamie said.

His parents were both interested in sport fishing and the conversation turned to rigs and lures.

Melissa smiled to herself watching the young boy

hang on Hunt's every word. Hunt is very good with Jamie, she mused. He's friendly but not condescending, lets Jamie express his opinions, and praises his ideas. He would probably make a wonderful father. *I wonder if he'll ever get married and settle down?* Try as she might, she couldn't conjure up an image of Hunt working nine-to-five in an office, commuting home to a big house in the suburbs with a two-car garage, and greeting children riding their bicycles in the driveway. But she could easily picture him teaching his son, or maybe even his daughter, to snorkel and fish and sail.

She heard the conversation veering in a new direction.

Jamie's mother sighed and said, "A week really isn't long enough to spend here. We need our own boat. We need to sail down here and stay for a few months or years."

Her husband agreed. "I know, we do. Too bad our thirty-footer isn't big enough. But I guess, until we can afford something larger, the Chesapeake will have to do."

"If we owned this boat, could we live here forever?" Jamie asked.

His father said, "If we owned this boat, we'd sail her to every island in the Caribbean, maybe twice." He glanced at Hunt. "We had some friends, Jake and Lynn Hendley, who did that. They spent three years cruising and went as far south as Venezuela."

Hunt nodded. "I wouldn't mind visiting South

America again myself. A boat like *Whitecap* is perfect for reaching along through the Windward and Leeward Islands. If she were mine, I'd arrange to do a season down there now and then."

Jamie turned to Melissa. "If you owned this boat, what would you do?"

The innocent question left Melissa momentarily stunned. She felt the blood drain from her face and her palms grow damp with sweat. She couldn't very well say that she would sell the boat and use the money to open a restaurant. And since being here, that idea had lost most of its appeal, anyhow.

She tried to answer but could only stammer. "I . . . I don't know, Jamie." She quickly placed her napkin on the table as she stood. "Hey, how about some dessert?"

She cleared away the plates and a few minutes later appeared with a tray of bananas and an extra-long wooden match that she used to ignite them. The rum burst into flame and drew applause from the diners. Watching as the fire slowly subsided, she had the unsettling thought that she was burning her bridges behind her. But the guests and Hunt were waiting for her next move, and she didn't have time to figure out whether that was good or bad.

Although the itineraries varied slightly, most charters included stops at popular locations that Melissa soon knew well. Each week they anchored *Whitecap* in Trunk Bay and Hunt deposited snorkelers at the marked underwater trail at Hawk's Nest. They cleared customs into the British Virgin Islands at Soper's Hole on Tortola and took their guests to the perfect beach at Sandy Cay. Usually the guests wanted to visit the infamous Foxy's Bar on Jost Van Dyke. The caves at the bight on Norman Island were always visited in the morning, giving Melissa time to prepare a lavish lunch. They usually stopped at the Baths on Virgin Gorda in the morning also, since the anchorage there could be treacherous in the peak afternoon winds. Day after day rushed by. And over and over again, they returned to Red Hook Bay, waved good-bye to smiling, sunburned faces, and then frantically reprovisioned and prepared for their next arrivals. It was demanding work, but as time passed, Melissa took more and more pleasure from helping people have a memorable vacation.

Every week Melissa wrote to Morgan. Each letter was filled with lively stories about the charters and the islands. She wrote about the flower-laden bushes and prickly cacti. She tried to find words to relate the beauty of the crystal-clear water. She described the bays, coves and beaches that *Whitecap* visited with her guests. But in all of her letters, she carefully avoided any mention of her feelings, or any possibility that she might return to North Carolina soon.

Christmas week was reserved for Hunt's friends, John and Vivien Myers. Five years ago, Hunt had been a star student at John's dive shop in Newport, Rhode

Island. For each of the past three years, John and Vivien had chartered this week on *Whitecap*. They had a standing reservation for years to come. Hunt brought them back from the airport and introduced them to Melissa.

"So, this is the lady with the fantastic brownies," Vivien remarked with a twinkle in her eye.

Melissa swept her puzzled eyes between Hunt and Vivien.

Vivien smiled and winked at Hunt. "I've been told you're an extraordinary cook who makes brownies almost as good as mine."

Hunt laughed and handed Melissa an open, Saran-wrapped box filled with colorfully decorated cookies and a few remaining chocolaty bars. "You're going to have a rough time for the next week," he told her. "Viv tries to take over the galley every time she's here. One of those cases in the tender is full of food and, if I guess right, there's a turkey defrosting somewhere in the middle of it."

Melissa liked the Myerses already. "Well, I sure hope everybody's hungry. Because it sounds like we're going to have plenty to eat."

Once they were settled, Vivien offered to help Melissa cook. "You simply have to give me something to do," she insisted.

Melissa resisted. "This is your vacation. You're not allowed to work."

Vivien was persistent and ready for objections. "That's nonsense. I like to help. And if I'm supposed to enjoy myself, then you're supposed to let me, it says so right in your brochure."

Melissa laughed, thinking she could still win. "It's a good argument, but the galley is only big enough for one person."

Vivien played her trump card. "It was big enough for me to help Myra three years running."

That piqued Melissa's curiosity. "Hunt hasn't said much about Myra. Was she a good cook?"

"She was very good." Vivien picked up a head of crisp lettuce and started breaking pieces into the salad bowl.

Melissa saw Vivien look at her with a sideways-glance and smile.

Vivien said, "I'm curious about why she quit, too."

Melissa felt a warm flush creep up her cheeks.

Vivien kept talking. "I imagine it had something to do with the fact that she was head over heels in love with Hunt, but didn't really like life on a boat. She tolerated it, but was constantly talking about moving ashore and living in New York City—that's where she grew up. Maybe she finally realized she could never get Hunt to change his lifestyle. I hope she wasn't hurt too badly."

Melissa remembered the turbulent emotion she'd seen in Hunt's eyes when Liz had asked about Myra on that first night at Langley's. She turned to stir the beefy onion soup and heard Vivien working at the lettuce again.

Vivien didn't miss a beat. "Even competing with

another woman is probably easier than trying to compete with a boat, I suppose. Two years ago I wondered why Hunt never married so I asked him about it, and do you know what he said?"

She paused and Melissa was surprised to realize she was actually waiting for an answer. Trying to keep her voice nonchalant, she turned around and quickly asked, "No, what did he say?"

Vivien patted her hand. "I knew you'd be interested. He said that he didn't need another love. That he already had *Whitecap*. You know, I wouldn't be surprised if Hunt never made a commitment to a woman. As long as he's got this boat, that's all he seems to want." She clicked her tongue several times then lowered her voice and leaned toward Melissa. "What a shame. Such a waste of a really wonderful guy. I can tell he's smitten with you though, so there may be hope for him yet."

Melissa laughed, although her stomach flip-flopped. She thought about the times over the past three months when a strange yearning and a light-headed feeling had come over her, watching Hunt as he skillfully sailed the boat or joked with the guests. And about how, every time they accidentally touched, she had to resist the urge to hold his hand, or run her fingers through his silky hair, or slip her arms around his waist and rest her cheek against his strong chest.

"We just work well together, that's all. That, plus I bake a lot of brownies." She took a deep breath and changed the subject. "So, tell me, what special dishes would you like to have for Christmas dinner?" She turned and removed the butterfly rolls from the hot oven. Then she tried to regain control of the salad, but Vivien wouldn't give up an inch of her hard-won foothold.

Christmas Eve they anchored in Leinster Bay, on the northern shore of the island of St. John. And at sunrise on Christmas Day, as Melissa watched a crab inch its way across the sand and rocks scattered below, the water was so amazingly clear that it seemed to disappear, giving her the impression that the boat was floating on air. The night before, they had all shared in decorating the boat for the holiday. Now, the combined effects of the water and decorations made her heart race in excitement, and gave *Whitecap* a magic-carpet feel and a fairy-tale look.

Even though Melissa woke up early to put the turkey in the oven, Vivien had already beaten her to it, and was busy fluting the edges of a pie crust around a mincemeat filling. Melissa chuckled at the sight of Vivien's green apron with a red Santa Claus and his reindeer stretched across her ample hips.

"Hunt certainly was right," Melissa said. "You are hard to discourage."

"I'm a homemaker. That's an important job to me. I enjoy doing what I do, and it makes me feel needed. I'd be lost if that was taken away from me."

"I know what you mean."

Melissa thought about Mr. Barnes and how needed

he had made her feel. Then she smiled as she realized that cooking aboard this boat made her feel good about herself. And that in a new way, it had given her a sense of being needed, too. She rolled the thoughts around in her head, wondering why she hadn't seen the truth before: she'd found a place to belong, the satisfying niche she'd been seeking.

She watched Vivien in contented silence for a minute, then made a suggestion. "Since it *is* my galley, may I help?"

Later, after they finished a sumptuous meal of turkey with all the trimmings, the two women chatted and worked side by side, cleaning up the dishes and singing along with the Christmas carols playing softly over the boat's stereo system.

John interrupted them. "Come on, Viv. Let's go snorkeling. I need some exercise after all that food."

"In a couple minutes," she told him. "We're almost done."

Melissa said, "Please go, Viv. I can finish this. You're making me feel guilty. You're spending your whole vacation working."

Vivien smiled. "We could both finish the work, then you could come with us."

"Oh, no. You two go ahead. I can see coral anytime."

A few minutes after Vivien left, Melissa heard bodies splashing into the water and voices growing more distant, then Hunt's footfalls as he came below.

"Umm. It still smells mouth-watering down here.

It's funny, turkey always reminds me of the big family get-togethers we had during the holidays when I was a kid." He looked sad for a mere second before he abruptly changed the subject. "Would you like a hand cleaning up?"

Melissa smiled at him, sympathizing with his thoughts of home. She remembered previous holidays, and recognized that, although Christmas usually made her feel melancholy and lonely, this year, sharing it with Hunt, she was feeling happy and content.

"Thank you very much, but actually, I'm done." She hung the dishtowel to dry.

He laughed. "Good, I must have timed it right then. That was a terrific meal."

"Thanks, but I can't take credit for all of it. Vivien did a lot of work, too."

He laughed. "She's like that. I know she didn't make the mango-nut bread, though. I recognized your hand in that. I think you should enter that in the next fleet cooking contest. And, of course, your pecan pie in the desserts category. Liz will be absolutely furious when you win."

"Maybe I'll do that. Liz may be gone by then, though. She's going to take that resort job in Miami. It's too bad, I was looking forward to competing against her."

"Well, you'll win regardless, I'm sure of that," he told her. "Anyway, I'm glad John and Viv left for a few minutes." He reached into his pocket and took out a small box with a bright red bow. A mischievous look sparkled in his eyes as he handed it to her. "Merry Christmas."

"Oh, Hunt, you didn't have to." She reached out, warmed by the pleasure of his thoughtfulness, and accepted the gift. It didn't matter to her what was in the box. The only thing of importance was that he wanted to give it to her.

Her pulse quickened as she undid the neat bow and removed the top of the box. She drew her breath in sharply at the sight of its contents.

"Oh, Hunt. It's absolutely gorgeous. Thank you, so much. How exquisite!"

Inside the box, a sparkling chain of finely woven silver strands rested on a bed of black velvet. When she lifted the chain, a tiny silver medallion hung suspended beneath it. Along the outer edge of the half-inch round disk, intricate filigree framed the center etchings of delicate, gracefully entwined roses. She held it carefully in her palm.

His eyes bore into hers, saying much more than his words. "The minute I saw it, I wanted it for you." He paused. "I'm glad you like it."

She lowered her eyes. She didn't dare to let him see the wild reaction that she was feeling in every cell of her body. Her hands felt awkward and were trembling as she undid the clasp and handed the chain to him. "Would you help me put it on?" She lifted the hair high off her neck, holding it up with both hands.

He took the chain and moved to behind her. There, he looped the chain around her neck and lowered it into place. She felt him fumble for a second with the tiny clasp in his large, masculine hands and, as he did, his fingers brushed her neck sending a tingling sensation pulsing down her back. Then he lightly smoothed the delicate chain down against her skin and rested his palms on her shoulders.

She silently gasped from the effect of his touch, her heart fluttering like the wings of a panicked bird. Her wavering voice was a traitor to her confused emotions. "Thank you again, Hunt. I've never seen anything more beautiful. This is the best gift, the best Christmas, I think I've ever had."

She waited for him to remove his hands, at the same time, deep inside, wishing he wouldn't. She closed her eyes. His closeness made her legs feel weak. Her mind told her to step away but her heart kept her body frozen in place. There was a long pause and then she heard the slow exhale of his breath. His hands withdrew and she stood with her back toward him for a minute longer. She clenched her jaw, desperately trying to conceal the emotion that she couldn't let him see.

When she lowered her hair and turned to face him, his eyes were veiled, hiding whatever he was feeling. She wondered if she had managed to do the same.

After a long awkward silence, she smiled. "Wait here a minute."

She went to her cabin and retrieved the silvery package she had wrapped very carefully the night before. A new hat seemed like a silly gift after the one he had given her, but she gave it to him anyway.

Chapter Nine

The day before the charter was to end, John and Vivien sat in the cockpit at sunset chatting with Hunt. Melissa brought out a tray of hot conch fritters with lime mustard dip and tiny sunburst tomatoes stuffed with guacamole. Hunt poured the cocktails and John proposed a toast.

"To another wonderful year," he offered. He sipped his drink and remarked to Hunt, "This week always seems to go by too fast. It's hard to believe it's time to leave already."

Hunt put down his glass and cleared his throat. "You know, there's a chance you may not be able to charter *Whitecap* next year," he said in a subdued voice.

John looked surprised and leaned forward. "Oh? Why's that?"

"Unfortunately, her owner, Mr. Barnes, died a few months ago. Once the estate is settled, she'll probably be put up for sale." Hunt's eyes revealed the sadness that was aroused by that thought. "She could get sold out of the charter business completely. But, even if it's just a new owner taking over, I expect things are going to change, me included. Nothing is definite yet, of course, but just in case, you may want to have an alternate plan for next Christmas."

"That would be a real shame," John sighed. "We look forward to this all year long. I'm not sure we could enjoy it as much on any other boat. And I know for sure we wouldn't want someone else as our captain. This must be quite a blow to you. What do you think you'll do if you lose this spot?"

Hunt shrugged his shoulders. "To tell you the truth, I'm not sure. Obviously, I could look for another job as a captain. But I've also considered buying a boat of my own, and maybe doing day charters or opening up a sailing school."

John looked thoughtful for a minute. "You told me at one time that you have an Inspected Vessel license, didn't you?"

"Yes, I do."

"Well, my dive shops run a liveaboard dive boat in the Florida Keys. It goes out for alternating four-day and one-week trips, taking up to ten people for two dives a day. We book all the trips at the dive shops, and send people down to either finish their certification or just do some fun dives." He sat back and crossed his legs. "The man we have running it right now is leaving at the end of the winter season. Would you like to come to work for me? You'd have a crew of three: a deck hand, a cook, and a dive instructor. You'd get two days off every second week. And the pay is guaranteed to be better than you're getting now."

Hunt looked taken aback. "I'm very tempted. It's an attractive offer. Working at a job like that for a few years I could easily save up enough to finance my own charter operation. But *Whitecap* may not sell for a while yet, and I wouldn't leave her until I had to. Do you need an answer right away?"

John shook his head. "No, no rush at all. I hadn't been planning on seriously looking for anybody for another couple months. Take all the time you need. If you want it, just let me know before, let's say . . . the middle of March."

Hunt nodded with a hint of sad resignation in his eyes. "Don't be surprised if you hear from me."

"I'll be looking forward to it," John replied, then the two men launched into a discussion of the SCUBA diving business in Florida and the Northeast.

Melissa listened to the exchange, but her mind was elsewhere. When she had taken Morgan's advice and agreed that when the estate was settled she would sell *Whitecap*, she hadn't considered that her decision would affect anyone else. Now, she was distressed to think that she was destroying Hunt's plans for the future. She recalled how Mr. Barnes's death had thrown her future into disorder. It seemed ironic that she was just now starting to regain her peace of mind, but that when *Whitecap* was sold, her own life would be set adrift all over again, too. Looking over and watching Hunt as he talked, she felt deep regret for what she was doing to him. She genuinely enjoyed being around him and working by his side. When they had to go their separate ways, she knew she would miss him dreadfully.

John got up and went below to search in his wallet for a picture of his dive boat.

After he left, Hunt turned toward Melissa and their eyes met. An electric shock coursed through her, sending a shiver down her spine and out to the tips of her toes. Her shoulders burned where he had rested his hands on Christmas Day. She could not remember ever experiencing such intense reactions to any man as those that Hunt sparked within her. He smiled warmly and she had the uncomfortable feeling that he knew exactly what she was thinking. She swallowed hard and averted her eyes.

When she looked up again, Vivien flashed her a confidential and knowing smile. "Too bad we don't serve anything fancier than cold sandwiches and burgers on the dive boats. It would be nice if we could offer you a job, too. Have you thought about what you might do?"

Melissa glanced at Hunt. She quickly turned away and wet her lips. "Ah, no, I haven't." She lifted her shoulders and dropped them again. "I guess I'll just figure it out when the time comes."

"Did you work on other boats before this one?"

"No. I worked at a resort in Atlanta for a while and then at a private estate."

"Maybe Hunt will be able to help you find another job." Vivien turned to Hunt, tilted her head, raised one eyebrow, and said, "I'll bet you know plenty of men, captains I mean, who are looking for somebody as pretty and talented as Melissa."

Hunt's forehead creased in a frown. "Probably."

"You two make such a good team, it would be a real shame to see you split up." Vivien looked up as John returned to the cockpit. "Put your thinking cap on, John. We need to find a way for Hunt and Melissa to stay together."

John sat down and affectionately squeezed Vivien's shoulder. "I'm afraid that's out of our hands, honey. Whoever owns this boat is going to pull those strings."

Melissa hung her head and fidgeted with the cuticle on her left thumb. *How long will it be before I have to do just that?*

The Myerses left, and Hunt and Melissa began the second half of the charter season. At the end of the first week, Hunt brought a large envelope from his cabin to take to the post office. For weeks he had labored in the nighttime privacy of his cabin drafting a letter to his father. The finished document outlined the financial details of the charter business, and proposed that his father approve an advance of funds from the trust for him to purchase *Whitecap*. Now, he held the letter in his hand and studied it. *Should I be putting this in the mail slot or the trash bin?* He reminded himself that he couldn't give up without a fight. *This is for* Whitecap. *I have to do everything possible to keep her.*

He recalled the last time he and his father had discussed the charter business. It had been an earnest conversation. But the elder man just didn't understand that service industry businesses operate under the very same principles as the manufacturing industries that his law firm represented. That was obvious when he remarked that Hunt wouldn't be enjoying his job so much if it was real work. Now, he was hoping that his father might overlook their differences of opinion long enough to study the data before he refused. Even if *Whitecap*'s new owner didn't think so, Hunt was sure that she was a good investment.

For several years, he'd wrestled with a decision concerning what he should do with the trust fund when it was released from his father's control. His younger brother dreamed of simply retiring in luxury with his share, but Hunt had decided on more ambitious plans. Eventually, the fleet of charter boats he envisioned was going to be a major competitor in the charter boat industry.

Melissa turned around and glanced his way. She

picked up a towel and dried her hands. "Are you stopping at the post office on your way to the airport?"

"Yes. Do you have anything you need mailed?"

"Unfortunately, yes. I need to get a check off to the place where my car is stored before they sell it for scrap. Can you wait just a second?"

"Sure." He watched her go to her cabin. If by some miracle he was able to buy the boat, there was no question about his plans for Melissa. She was the best thing that had happened to him in a long time. He wanted her to stay on and keep working with him, even if he had to struggle to pay her salary.

It's unfair that she should have to suffer because of something beyond her control. I should have told her when she took the job that this whole thing could blow up at any moment.

He realized that he felt protective toward her. He could never send her away where she might not be safe and secure. He chuckled to himself at the thought. Life on a boat was hardly safe and secure. But he would do everything in his power to shield her from being an innocent victim when the ownership of *Whitecap* changed.

She walked back into the cabin licking then pressing shut the flap on an envelope. "Here you go. Thanks for waiting."

He took her letter, tucked it in his pocket, and bowed low at the waist. "Your wish is my command, fair lady."

She laughed. "Well, in that case . . ."

He straightened and held up a hand to halt her words. "Whoa, forget I said that. I'm outta here."

Later, he pushed his bulky envelope through the mail slot. The tension he felt in his neck and shoulders disappeared as soon as it slid out of sight.

The last week in January, they had an extra day between charters. It was a Saturday and Melissa was anxious to go into town and shop at the open-air market. When she told Hunt of her plans, he decided to go along.

Melissa always felt a surge of excitement when her eyes took in the chaotic scene. The center of town was crowded with small stalls and tables where vendors were marketing their wares. Toothless old women sat under brightly colored umbrellas tending baskets heaped with garden-grown fruits and vegetables. Young men in dreadlocks hawked rap and reggae CDs. Pretty young mothers, with children clinging to their legs, displayed straw goods and souvenir T-shirts. And everywhere young children dashed wildly through the streets.

Hunt waved to a group of boisterous fishermen who stood smoking and exchanging insults while their catch waited on a bed of ice for a purchaser. "I'm going to go over and visit with Dunstan and his friends. Let me know if you need a hand with anything."

"Okay. It will probably take me a while to find the ingredients I'm looking for."

They parted and Melissa took her tote bags and wove through the crowd. She spotted the woman she called "the spice lady" and approached her table. Fresh basil leaves that had been bundled into Zip-loc bags were piled next to small jars of fresh curry spice and tangy cinnamon. A deep basket held loose nutmegs in the shells that were sold by the handful. Vanilla beans hung from a makeshift rack. The smells that filled the air were exotic and delicious. Melissa spied some packets of jira seed, the essential ingredient for making rotis, and saffron, which she hadn't been able to find anywhere else. Before she moved on, she purchased a generous supply of each, along with a large ginger-root and some cloves.

Next, she headed for the vegetable vendors. Some of the produce was over-ripe or bruised. But she squeezed, snapped, tapped and sniffed. When she made her selections, she was satisfied that they were at the peak of flavor. Soon, she'd filled one of her bags to overflowing with a diverse assortment of local products.

She saw the bright red turban worn by her favorite fruit vendor two rows away and passed by several other beckoning vendors, in order to reach the woman's booth. Once there, she waited for her friend to finish with another customer, inspecting the display of mangos while she did.

When the woman was free, she turned to Melissa and smiled. "Good day, Missy. How are you this fine morning?"

"Wonderful, Mrs. Blair. And how are you?"

"Fine, fine. My fruits are selling fast today. I'll be able to get my daughter Tessa that fancy pair of shoes that she's been yearning for by the time we close at noon."

"I'm glad for her, but not for me. You don't have much left."

Mrs. Blair smiled broadly. "Don't you fret, now. I sensed you'd be here today and I kept aside a bag of my best mangoes for you." She reached under the table and set a paper sack on the counter. "They're sweet and rosy pink, just the way your man likes them. I know how hard you try to please him."

Melissa felt her cheeks growing warm. "Thank you very much, but he's not really my man. He's just the captain of the boat that I work on."

"Now, now. You know I can tell fortunes and have the power to feel things about people. And I sense I'm right. There's an aura around you when he's near. Fact is, you know where he is right now without even looking." She pointed a bony finger across the table. "Isn't that true?"

Melissa flipped her hair back over her shoulder. "Well, it's only logical that he would be done talking to the fishermen by now. And that when he left there he would wander over to browse the boat gear."

"It's not logic, Missy. You know because you can sense his presence. There's a bond between you. You should let me do a reading of the cards. Free, because we are friends. I could see a lot more."

"Thank you, but I don't think so." She didn't want to tell the woman that she didn't believe in the fortune telling, magic, and voodoo that was an integral part of the island culture.

"As you wish. I know a lot of young people don't believe in the powers."

Melissa examined a papaya, held it up to Mrs. Blair, who nodded, and then put it into her empty tote bag. "I know what the cards would say, anyhow. Hunt and I are good friends. But we don't have a future together."

"I can't tell you the future unless you ask. But you don't need to worry. He feels the attraction too. He is here to protect you and help you."

The laugh that Melissa forced had a nervous edge, even to her own ears. "He's here to visit the fishermen."

Mrs. Blair laughed, too. "So you think. But he cares about your welfare. And you repay him by caring about his stomach."

Melissa paid for her purchases and arranged the fragile mangoes carefully in her bag. In addition to the papaya, she'd found a pineapple, some plantains, six limes, six lemons, and several guavas and oranges. Both her bags bulged now. She grunted as she lifted them from the ground.

A scent of familiar aftershave reached her at the same instant that Hunt's strong hands relieved her of her burdens. "Let me have those, they look heavy."

"I can manage."

"No you can't. They're too heavy for you. You'll strain yourself. Here, you can carry this if you want to help."

He set down one bag, and handed her a plastic wrapper that he unhooked from his thumb. It was cold where she felt the bottom. "What is it?"

"Grouper fillets packet in ice. A freebie courtesy of Dunstan. He had a good catch."

"Wonderful, we'll grill them tonight. But I hate to take his fish for free. He has such a big family to feed."

"The people here share with their neighbors when they have extra. When they're in need, it comes back to them in kind."

"Maybe we could invite him and his family out to the boat some night for dinner. I'd love to meet his wife."

"Sure, if we ever get another day off. Meanwhile, I'm going to gather together some of those lures that we need to replace. I can drop them off at his house next time I'm in town. He's a resourceful guy. He'll shine and paint them up and be able to use them for years."

They stepped clear of the crowd and headed for the taxi stand. There was a shout and instantly, Hunt, tote bags and all, jumped between Melissa and the baseball that was speeding toward her head. He dropped to the ground after deflecting the ball with his shoulder.

"Oh, Hunt. Are you all right?"

He sat in the fruit, winced and rotated his arm.

"Yeah. I'll survive. Whoever launched that has a killer pitch, though."

A teenaged boy rushed up to them. His eyes were wide with fear and big as saucers. "Sorry, mister. I didn't see you until after I threw."

Hunt got to his feet and gave a reassuring squeeze to the boy's shoulder. "You've got a heck of a throwing arm there, son. But be a little more careful next time, would you? You could have hurt the lady here real bad."

"I'm sorry. We'll go somewhere else. Farther away from the crowd."

"Good idea." Hunt turned to Melissa. "You okay?"

"Me? Sure. Thanks to you."

Grinning, Hunt said, "I can't very well have you unconscious in some hospital for the next week, can I?"

"Does it hurt bad?"

He shook his head. "It's nothing." But when he reached down to pick up the heavy tote bags, he winced again.

"I'd better carry that," Melissa said. "And as soon as we get into a taxi, I'm going to put that iced fish on your shoulder. The cold will make you feel better."

"Use the ice, but not the fish. I want that in my stomach."

Melissa heard Mrs. Blair's words again. "He cares about your welfare. And you repay him by caring about his stomach." She wondered if that had been an observation or a prediction. And what else could Mrs.

Blair see if she asked her to look? No one could foretell the future, it was just a coincidence, she decided. And even if it were possible, nothing would change. Aura or not, Hunt couldn't be a lasting part of her life.

Hunt loaded the bags into the trunk and climbed into the taxi beside her. When she pressed the ice against his bruised shoulder, he reached up and placed his hand over hers for a few seconds before she took it away. "Thanks, Missy. I appreciate your caring."

Her heart faltered as if it had skipped several beats. It would be so easy right now to lean forward and kiss him. She said softly, "I can't very well have you incapacitated for the next week, can I? Who'd do all the hard work?"

The twinkle in his blue eyes reminded her of the sun playing on the ocean. "Aye, I've been tellin' me mates that all along. You're a heartless wench, you are."

She imitated his dialect. "Mind yer tongue there, me captain, or me fist might slip and bash that injured limb."

"It'll be mutiny next, I swear. I'll have me eye on you from now on, lass."

"There's many ways to get the ship. I'll run you through with me cutlass and you'll never see it coming," she said.

"You'll never wrest *Whitecap* away from me. I'll fight for her until I draw the last of me breath."

Covering her mouth with her hand, Melissa turned abruptly toward the window. *Yes, I believe he would.*

                          *   *   *

In the middle of February, Morgan's letter to Melissa was unusually thick. Inside she found a packet of legal documents and a handwritten note:

My darling Melissa,

  Since Ross Barnes dropped his challenge, probate has been concluded swiftly. The estate has been settled and the boat is now legally yours. Only a couple minor business issues have changed, but nothing you need to be concerned about. As long as I have your power of attorney, I can take care of everything necessary for you and proceed as per our plans.

                        Come home soon.
                        All my love, Morgan

Melissa read the letter through twice. *Whitecap* was hers.

She folded the papers and sat looking around her snug cabin. A leaden feeling settled around her heart. Now that she owned the boat, she would have to sell it. Morgan had studied the financial statements. He'd said that chartering was a risky business. She wasn't rich. She couldn't support a yacht. If the boat didn't have a successful season, she wouldn't even have enough money to pay the operating expenses.

She wondered if there was any way to keep the boat. *Hunt loves it so much. I don't want to take it away from him. We're a good team.* She decided to ask Morgan for copies of the financial statements so that she could see for herself whether or not the boat was making a profit.

Her thoughts returned to Hunt and she drew in a deep breath. *I can tell him now. But how do I do that after all this time? How can I explain?* She bit on her lower lip and stared into near space searching for an answer. Her mind churned for several minutes, but she found no magic phrases that would make him understand.

Melissa stuffed the papers into her top drawer and went back to organizing her meal plan for the coming week. The new guests were vegetarians, who also chose not to eat dairy products, and trying to serve well-balanced and interesting meals, with such a limited choice of ingredients, posed a real challenge. And right now, she felt much more comfortable immersing herself in menus rather than thinking of what the future might hold.

Chapter Ten

Three weeks later Hunt went ashore and returned with a grim expression.

"Good news and bad news, Missy."

She looked up from folding the freshly laundered dinner napkins and watched him swing his muscular frame onto the port settee. "Good news first, please."

"Okay. The good: we have next week off. The bad: it's because we've had a cancellation. Roger also said their check bounced. So we've lost our chance at a one hundred percent paid season."

She stopped her work, and tried not to look as shaken as she felt. "Oh, that is bad."

"Serious bad. Especially to the accountants. Last year, business was really off and Mr. Barnes lost a bundle. This year, I was hoping we could prove that

Whitecap can still make a go of it, keep the wolves from the door, so to speak."

"Mr. Barnes?" Melissa was surprised to hear his name again. But then it made sense. *Of course. They must have known each other. I wonder why I didn't think of that before. Hunt must be the "young man" Mr. Barnes spoke about in some of his stories.*

Hunt explained. "Yeah. Didn't I ever tell you about him? He was a really great old guy. He was *Whitecap*'s owner until he died a few months back. When I first took this job, he used to come down here once in a while and sail her himself." He smiled broadly and shook his head. "The guy was in his late sixties, but I had a hard time keeping up with him. I remember one night in a bar in Nassau, he . . . well, ah . . . never mind." His voice trailed off and his smile went flat. "Now, we've got some new landlubber owner who's only interested in dollar signs."

Melissa was silent and she cast her eyes toward the floor. *I have to explain to him that I'm the new owner. He's got to understand that I'm not some millionaire who can shrug off a loss as a tax deduction. I can't afford the boat's upkeep, or even pay his salary. I have to tell him, but how?*

"Hunt, I have to—" The oven timer began to buzz and she blew out a heavy breath. "Just a second." She darted across the cabin and turned off the stove.

When she returned he had brightened a little. "Anyway," he said, "for the next week you and I are on a mini-vacation of sorts. Time to catch up on some of the maintenance."

"Sounds good to me." Melissa sighed, pushing thoughts of the "landlubber owner" from her mind. She liked things the way they were and didn't want their near-perfect relationship to change. *I have to tell him and I will tell him soon, but not right now.*

Hunt's expression became serious. "I appreciate how hard you've had to work to learn the ropes. Tell you what, for starters, let's declare the rest of today a holiday. Why don't you jump into a swimsuit? I'll show you a secret little beach I know with absolutely, guaranteed, no tourists."

She was surprised and thrilled that he would want to spend his day with her. "You're on."

She hummed as she went below to change. In her cabin, she unbraided, and then brushed out, her hair. It felt wonderful to be out of her uniform. Wearing white shorts and a sky blue polo shirt every day had become boring. She realized that it had been months since she'd worn anything else.

The tender sped across the crystal-clear water and Hunt aimed the bow at a picture-postcard beach that he had discovered a few years before. From the land, he knew it was possible for a lost motorist to stumble across the abandoned tiki bar that was partly obscured by wildly overgrown vegetation. But the tiny beach, where sea grapes and fragrant, blossom-laden bougainvillea ringed the fine, white sand, was a treasure that he hoped no one else would ever find.

They spent the first part of the afternoon lazing in the tropical sun. Later, Hunt produced a Frisbee and they tossed it between them until he was exhausted and they collapsed on the sand. Melissa propped herself up, leaned back on her elbows, and breathed heavily.

Hunt looked closely at her beautifully flushed face and was struck by a tidal wave of emotion. *I can't deny it any longer. I care about her. I want to be with her all the time. And not just for now. My efforts to stay detached have failed miserably. She affects me differently than any other woman I've ever met.*

Suddenly, it dawned on him that there was no longer a compelling reason not to get emotionally involved. *Whitecap* could be sold at any time, and then they would no longer be working together as her crew.

Melissa hung her head back with her eyes closed and her hair brushing the sand. He shifted his weight to lean toward her. He focused his eyes on her lips. An unusually large wave crashed at their feet, spraying them with grainy droplets of sand and water.

Melissa squealed. She jumped up, laughed, and shook her arms, throwing off the blotchy spots of sand as she ran into the water. "Looks like we may as well take a swim."

When he didn't get up immediately, she pushed the palms of her hands into the backs of the waves, splashing sheets of water in his direction.

Hunt jumped up and rushed toward her, but she laughed again and dove into the sea, escaping his grasp. She swam out a few strokes but his strokes were stronger. He caught up with her and dove below her. Grabbing her ankle, he pulled her under for just long enough to make his point. He bobbed to the surface and she came up sputtering next to him.

"Had enough?" he asked with his hand poised over her head.

She caught her breath and glanced upward. "Yes! I give up. You win."

He pulled his hand away and grinned wickedly. "Smart move. Tell you what, if you want to swim, why don't I get the snorkeling gear out of the tender? There's some fantastic coral on the other side of those outer rocks."

She agreed enthusiastically. They donned dive masks, snorkels, and swim fins, and swam across the tiny bay.

The small reef did not disappoint her. The rocks in the area were lovely, seemingly painted from a spectacular palette of vibrant colors by numerous colonies of the tiny, living corals. Tube sponges and a grouping of feathery gorgonians swayed and bowed in the undulating sea. Large stalks of elkhorn coral steadfastly guarded the beach, acting like a seawall built only inches below the water's surface. Miniature reef fish darted in and out of the pockets and valleys of the formation. Wide-eyed queen angelfish and yellowtail damselfish studied them warily as they swam over-head. Hunt tapped her on the shoulder and pointed to a large sea turtle lazily gliding by fifteen feet away. Beyond him, shafts of sunlight radiated through the aquamarine water bathing the scenery in a magical glow.

Much later, they emerged from the water. Melissa stretched out on the warm sand like a contented kitten. Hunt sat beside her with his arms crossed on his knees.

She sighed. "These islands are so wonderful I can see why people would want to stay here forever."

"As long as the trade winds are blowing, they're fine. But they can get pretty hot. In the summer months the trades die down, and anywhere out of the breeze is like an inferno. That's part of why it's the off season. That and the threat of hurricanes."

"Is that why you take *Whitecap* up to New England?"

"Sure is. That's where the vacationers want to be. The weather up there in the summer is much more comfortable. Of course, the water is cold and the wind isn't as predictable as it is here, but it has its own charm. Ever been to Newport?"

"No. But I've seen pictures of The Breakers and the other mansions, and some coverage on TV during the America's Cup races years ago."

"You'll like it," Hunt said. "It's a great big harbor crammed full of boats from all over the world. It's a quaint New England seafaring town that's grown too big, but somehow it hasn't changed. Boaters are still welcome and they congregate there for all sorts of races and events."

He chuckled. "Newport's where I first met Mr. Barnes, in a little informal race between his tender and mine. We both got reprimanded by the harbor police for creating a wake. He won."

"It sounds like the two of you had some good times together. Is that when you got the job on *Whitecap*?"

"Shortly after that."

Melissa looked down at the sand and tried to wet her lips, but her tongue felt suddenly dry. "Hunt, do you believe that Mr. Barnes had a good reason for leaving the boat to the person he chose to have her?"

"Yeah, I guess, unless he was getting senile. But who knows? The guy I remember was a smart cookie. He managed to do some pretty eccentric things sometimes, but they always worked out in the end. Figuring out his reasons was a real brain teaser, though."

Melissa took a deep breath and opened her mouth to speak.

But Hunt kept talking. "Too bad you couldn't have met him. He would have liked you. Anyhow, enough of that. I don't want to hear one more word about Mr. Barnes. It makes me think about the new owner, and I get upset."

"Hunt, about the new owner—"

"Don't remind me about that landlubber. I'm trying to relax. Let's get back to Newport." He smirked. "Unless, of course, you want another dunking?"

She sighed. "Okay, Newport. You once said you're

originally from Connecticut. Did you live far from Newport?"

"Home is a town called Essex on the Connecticut River. From Newport it's about a three-hour drive by car or a full day's sail by boat. Maybe in-between charters we can get up that way. It's a real nice trip up the river in the fall when the foliage changes color."

The thought crossed her mind that she would enjoy seeing Essex and Newport, but she might not get the chance. *Whitecap* could be sold by then. She knew she would be disappointed if that happened. "Do you still have family there?"

His eyes clouded over. "Yes, my folks, a brother, and my sister and her kids."

"You must miss them being so far away."

"Only my sister. It would be good to see her again. Kim and I were always close and she was the only one in the family on my side when I wanted to quit law school and join the Navy."

She sensed his reluctance to talk about his family. But she was always curious about the childhood experiences of other people. Her childhood had ended abruptly when her mother died. "Was Essex a good place to grow up?"

Hunt thought for a minute. "I suppose so. It's a small town where everyone knows everyone else. In the winter it's quiet and the residents are clannish and straight-laced. In the summer, the tourists and boat people invade by the thousands and everything's out of control. That's confusing when you're growing up."

Melissa rolled onto her side, placing her elbow on the hard sand. Then she rested her chin on her hand. "How's that?"

He looked up and she followed his eyes to a lone puffy, white cloud that stood out boldly against the bright blue sky. "I guess you could say it's like living in two different worlds. One with strict moral values and a feeling of community, and another where the dollar bill reigns supreme over everything else. You see people put on new faces depending on the season, and it makes you all too aware of how much of life is a charade. People pretend to be happy. Husbands and wives pretend love that went cold years before. Businessmen pretend they think success is more important than money. Everywhere you look, someone is pretending to be something they're not.

"My mother was the greatest pretender of all. At one time, my grandfather built quite an empire in southern Connecticut." A flicker of a smile touched his lips. "I remember when I was a kid I believed he owned the whole state." The smile faded. "Of course, he didn't. But he owned enough of it to amass a rather large fortune. Because of his wealth and the fact that my father is a successful lawyer, my mother thought we had a social position, as she called it. She used to tell me all the time when I was growing up that, as Huntington Stewart III, I had a responsibility to live up to my name. That I couldn't associate with just anyone. She sent me to stuffy private schools where I would meet all the right people"—he winced when he said the words—"for more years than I care to think about."

He stopped and Melissa waited in silence. Her thoughts dwelled on how deeply she missed not having the love of a family. She found it difficult to understand the obvious alienation he felt toward his.

"Anyway," he went on, "it showed me how I *don't* want to live my life. I can look at the ocean and know what I see is real. That's the way I like it. I can get up every morning and be myself. I don't have to feel like I'm on a stage where no one is what they're pretending to be. The ocean doesn't tolerate pretend sailors."

Neither of them spoke for a long time after he finished talking. Melissa closed her eyes and tried to ignore the churning in her stomach as she lay thinking. She decided that right now wouldn't be a good time to tell Hunt about *Whitecap*'s new owner.

When they got back to *Whitecap* at dusk, the trade winds had fallen unusually calm and Melissa could see a mirror image of the boat reflected off the silvery surface of the smooth water. Even the usual hustle on shore seemed subdued, almost as if the lack of a breeze had becalmed the land as well.

"I'm going to run those two empty SCUBA tanks over to the dive shop before they close," Hunt told her. "We may want to use them in the next couple days. Tell you what, instead of you cooking tonight, how about when I get back we go out and attack an extra large pizza with the works?"

"You're chock full of great ideas today, aren't you? I need to soak my sunburn for a few minutes, but after that, I think I could eat a horse."

"I don't know if that's on the topping list, but we can ask."

After Hunt left, Melissa decided to repay his thoughtfulness. She dashed into the galley to mix up a batch of his favorite brownies. Measuring the ingredients from memory, she stirred the flour, sugar, eggs, cocoa, butter, and vanilla into a gooey batter, then added an extra large portion of halved walnuts. Then she spread the batter into a pan and slipped the pan into the oven.

She went to her cabin and carefully removed her sandy, damp swimsuit then luxuriated in the shower. The stylish, high-cut legs had left her sunburned in uncomfortable places. She lathered her hair twice and rinsed it thoroughly, then let the cool water neutralize the heat of her skin and refresh her parched pores.

"Oh!" Her eyes shot wide open. "The brownies! They'll burn!"

She scrambled into her clothes and then raced toward the galley with her hair dripping a trail behind.

She yanked the pan from the oven, and at the same instant, heard Hunt bring the tender to the stern of the boat.

"Hey, something smells great down here."

She placed the pan on a rack to cool. As she turned,

she was hugged, lifted off her feet and kissed exuberantly on the mouth. It was all so fast and fluid that she had no time to react.

"You must have been reading my mind. I've been craving brownies all afternoon."

She grinned at him. "Wow! I think you'd better put me down."

He had a mischievous twinkle in his eyes. "Why? I like this position."

The glow on his face caused a fluttering in her chest. "Well, ah, . . . for one thing, I'm getting you wet."

"I don't mind."

He set her feet on the floor, but stayed close beside her. For a long minute they stared into each other's eyes. Then, his hands cupped her face. He brought his mouth towards hers and brushed her lips with a feather-soft kiss. Her arms slipped around his neck. He murmured her name, twined his fingers through her hair, and then tenderly pressed his lips to hers.

For a long, magical moment she enjoyed the tantalizing sensation of his mouth moving on hers. Her soul seemed to melt into the pleasant cocoon of his arms. Then, reality intruded. She began to tremble. *I can't let this happen. I have to get this situation back under control.*

She put her hands on his chest and pushed him away. "You shouldn't do that." She struggled to resist the impulse to pull him back.

His voice was soft. His eyes filled with determination. "Yes I should. I should have done it a long time ago. I can't stop myself any longer, Missy. There's something special happening between us."

She took a deep breath. "I like you, Hunt. We work well together. That doesn't necessarily mean anything more."

Hunt put his fingers under her chin and whispered, "You're lying to both of us, you know. Your words aren't telling me the same thing your lips did a minute ago." He paused and slowly traced her bottom lip with his thumb. "But, as much as I dislike it, I can accept your protests for now. I can wait until you're ready to admit how you feel."

She gazed into the deep blue of his eyes. It was impossible for her to deny the feelings that had been growing within her for months. She longed to be in his arms, free from her own nagging fears. She swallowed hard, fighting to regain her composure.

A grin spread across his face. The look in his eyes didn't match the disappointed tone of his voice. "Anyway, can I still buy you that pizza?"

She flashed him a small smile of relief. "You don't get any dessert unless you do."

That night, after they returned to *Whitecap* and went to their cabins, Melissa climbed into her bunk but lay wide awake. She was frightened by her attraction to Hunt but haunted by the pleasure of his kiss. *Love always hurts. I can't let it happen again.*

She fell into a brief dream-filled sleep. Over and

over again a vision kept returning of Hunt running toward her, then sweeping her into his arms. Each time, she gave her heart to him completely in exchange for the feel of his lips and his warm embrace.

She awoke, tortured by her own thoughts. Deep inside she craved the very affection that she resisted most. She felt like a person dying of thirst in the desert who had found water, but was afraid to drink for fear of poisoning. She resolved that, until she could be certain whether Hunt was her poison or her salvation, she wouldn't let him any closer to her heart.

Chapter Eleven

T he next day, Hunt got a message to call Roger. He dialed the number and recognized the voice on the other end of the line. "Hey, Rog, what's up?"

Roger sounded hesitant. "I thought you'd want to know, Hunt. The new owner may have a buyer."

The words struck Hunt like a bolt of lightning, the thunder crashing his world down around him. "How sure is it?"

"Sounds like they've ironed out most of the details. They're seen all the promotional videos, but, of course, they still have to inspect the boat. That's probably just a formality though."

Hunt stared into space trying to absorb the news. He was certain that anyone seeing *Whitecap* would want to own her. Then he heard Roger say, "Listen,

Hunt, I found something else out yesterday. I think you should know."

"After that bombshell, what else matters?"

"Morgan Black called me to bring me up-to-date. He mentioned the name of the new owner."

Hunt's head snapped up. "Did you say Morgan Black?"

"Yeah. He's one of the lawyers who handled Old Man Barnes's estate."

Hunt had a sick feeling in the pit of his stomach. He spoke to himself more than to Roger. "Now I remember."

Roger continued. "Anyway, he told me who *Whitecap*'s new owner is. You'd better hang on to your hat."

"Why?"

"It's Melissa."

Hunt heard the name echo in his head, like he was dreaming. "Melissa? Missy? Come on. No way. What kind of a line are you giving me, Rog?" But, even as he said the words, Morgan Black's return address emblazoned on Melissa's letters burned like a branding iron in his mind's eye.

"No line. It's true, Hunt. She worked for Old Man Barnes while he was dying. He gave *Whitecap* to her in his will."

Hunt swayed with the shock waves as his world continued to explode apart. The boat he loved was almost sold. He had cared for her as if she had been his own. She was going to be the queen of his charter fleet. But now, instead, *Whitecap* would be taken from him. And Melissa, of all people, was responsible. He spoke as if in a daze. "Missy owns *Whitecap* and she's selling her?"

He dropped the phone and left it dangling by the cord. When the numbness in his brain subsided, he was standing on the dock next to his tender without knowing how he'd gotten there. Then he started the motor and headed back to *Whitecap*. Now all the questions he had about Melissa on that first day had answers.

Melissa was polishing a bronze oil lamp when he stomped into the main cabin.

"Well, you've done it, haven't you?" he said, as he entered. He stopped with his feet planted apart and his fists on his hips. "All this time I thought you were special. Now I find out I've just been a fool."

"Hunt, what—?"

"You've put on quite a performance, lady boat owner. I thought I could spot a phony a mile away. But I really fell for your I'm-just-a-cook act."

She jumped up and crossed to him, clutching his forearm. "Hunt, please. Let me explain."

He shook off her touch, furious with himself for letting her spark a deep yearning for her even now. "Explain! Explain what? That all along *Whitecap* has been your boat. That I've been the hired hand. And now you've finally gone and betrayed both of us. How could you act so dedicated then turn around and sell this proud, beautiful lady to strangers?"

"Sell? *Whitecap is* for sale, but—"

"Oh, please. Don't insult me any more with the fake surprise."

"It's not fake. Hunt, please. Listen to me."

"Listen to you? Yeah, right. What are you going to say? That you're not selling *Whitecap*? That you really didn't know Mister Barnes?" He narrowed his eyes and compressed his lips.

She threw up her hands. "I did know him, yes. I never said I didn't."

"No. You just sat here in this cabin and *acted* like you didn't. Congratulations, you put that one over on me good."

"I just couldn't tell you. Not at first."

"You couldn't tell me? You could make up all kinds of stories to dance around the truth, but you couldn't tell the truth? You know, that's the part that galls me the most. You're just like all the rich women I've ever met. You've got a bundle of dough so you think you can throw common courtesy to the wind. And if you trash someone else's life along the way, who cares?"

"I'm not rich. And I didn't mean to upset your life."

"Well, for somebody who didn't have that intention, you're sure doing a great job." He thought about how he'd wanted to protect her and almost laughed out loud at his stupidity. Instead of worrying about her well being, he should have been guarding his own.

"Will you please let me explain why I'm here?"

"Sure, why are you here? Are you looking for reasons to fire me so you can hire somebody else who'll work cheaper?"

"No, Hunt. I think you're the perfect captain for *Whitecap*. I think you're a wonderful person."

His thoughts raced. *I used to think you were more than wonderful. And what about when I kissed you? Were you playing a game then? Was I not good enough to touch you? Was I just somebody who works on a boat? Somebody whose hands get dirty?* "Just answer me one thing. Why couldn't you even tell me yourself?"

Melissa opened her mouth.

The blood pounded in his ears. *She's been treating me like a fool and I've been too infatuated to notice. What's the matter with me? Am I crazy, standing here, expecting the truth?* Hunt cut her off.

"No! Don't answer that. I don't think I want to know, Miss Catterly. As of this minute, I formally quit as captain of your boat. Obviously, you and *Whitecap* don't need my services anymore. I'll be moving off immediately."

Hunt turned and stomped away from her. In his cabin, he began gathering his things. It felt good to open and slam drawers and doors. He hurled some of his clothes onto the berth, then punched them mercilessly into a duffel bag. His eyes scanned around him but there were no clear thoughts in his mind. He zipped the bag shut. Then unzipped it again and tossed in a toothbrush, a comb, and his shaver.

"I'll send for the rest of my stuff later," he informed her as he left. "Roger can hold my final check."

He dumped his bag into the tender and paused for a few seconds before casting off the line. *No, I won't go back. I won't let her make a fool out of me again.* He started the motor and sped toward shore.

She took a step after him, but he was gone. Melissa stood alone silently staring at the empty cabin steps. A lump formed in her throat and she swallowed hard. Her entire body felt as if it was cast in stone. She didn't want him to go, but she was powerless to stop him. *Why didn't I tell him before he found out from someone else? Why did I put it off until it was too late? How could I have done this to him?* She bit at her lower lip until it hurt and shut her eyes, drawing her breath in deeply. She fought the tears that welled behind her eyelids.

Her heart leaped when she first heard the outboard motor. But then, she recognized that the sound was not *Whitecap*'s tender. Her realization that he wasn't coming back caused a shiver of fear. She tried to tell herself she was only upset because of *Whitecap*, because it was the middle of the season, but she knew that it was because of Hunt.

She heard a knock on the hull and went on deck. When she got to the cockpit, Erich was standing in his own tender near *Whitecap*'s stern, putting a line on a cleat.

"Just ran into Hunt ashore. He asked me to run your

tender back out to you." His tone was inquisitive. "He seemed rather upset."

Melissa felt like she was suffocating and drew in a long breath. "We both are."

He came aboard uninvited. "That's pretty evident from the look on your face. What happened?"

She fought back tears. "Hunt just quit."

His eyes opened wide. "Hunt? Quit *Whitecap*? Now, in the middle of the season? I can't believe it."

"Oh, it's quite true," Melissa assured him. Her eyes scanned the shore for a glimpse of Hunt. "It seems I'll have to find *Whitecap* another captain."

Erich's eyebrows shot up. "You? Why should you have to find a captain?"

"It's a long story, but you may as well know. I own *Whitecap*." She offered no more explanation although he looked at her quizzically.

"You *own Whitecap*?" He pursed his lips for a long minute. "A new captain, huh? Well, I can't think of anybody available right now. I can check around in town and contact a few friends for you, though. Maybe someone will turn up."

"I'd appreciate that. I don't even know where to start," Melissa said absently. Every cell in her body seemed to be shouting a chorus in her ears: *I don't want another captain, I want Hunt.*

Erich crossed his legs and settled back into the cockpit cushions. "You know, of course, that anyone you get needs at least a six-passenger license. Coast Guard regulations require that in U.S. waters. A check of their references wouldn't hurt. Good captains don't float from job to job. There's an agency in town, Crews Unlimited, that deals with crew placements. They've got a good reputation. You might give them a ring."

"Yes. Thanks. I'll try them," Melissa said. Her mind was wandering. She worried about Hunt and the anguish he must be feeling.

Erich smiled at her. "Actually, it's too bad I have a contract on *Crystal Lady*. There's nothing I'd like better than to take the job myself. I've wanted to get onto a bigger boat for a while now, especially since Liz quit. This new girl is nowhere near as good. Our customer satisfaction ratings are slipping. *Whitecap* would be a nice step up." He leaned toward her. "What if I break my contract?"

"*Whitecap* is for sale, maybe even sold. What would you do in a month or two?"

"Oh." Erich sighed. "I didn't know that. I suppose I'd better stay where I am then. Too bad, we could have been a great team." He slid over beside her, then took her hand and ran his fingers lightly up her arm. "You know, in a way I'm glad Hunt quit. I'm a very sore loser and something tells me he was making better progress with you than I am. But now, with him out of the way, I can have you all to myself."

Melissa pulled her hand away. She recalled the warmth of Hunt's touch the night before. "I told you once already, Erich, I'm not looking for a relationship."

"Yes, I know. But, you see, that makes you even more of a challenge. Success will be just that much sweeter."

She tried to smile, but deep inside, she had the feeling that he was actually serious.

"Why don't I help you forget your problems tonight?" Erich went on. "Let's go to that new place next to Langley's for dinner. Give me a chance to win your heart."

Melissa only wanted to be alone. "Thank you anyway, but I didn't sleep well last night. I'm very tired." She shook her head from side to side. "Besides, I don't think I'd be very good company tonight. I'll just stay here."

His eyes held a look of determination. "If you like, but remember, I'm not easily discouraged."

"Go away, Erich." She closed her eyes, no longer able to be polite. "Just go away."

The receptionist at McKinley, McKinley, Bayer, Fitzgerald and Black put Melissa right through to Morgan.

"Melissa, darling, how wonderful to hear from you. You've just made my day."

"It's good to hear your voice," she replied politely. She hadn't spoken to him in months, and somehow he seemed like a stranger.

"You must have ESP or something. I've some good news for you," he went on.

"I could use some."

Morgan didn't seem to notice her terse mood. He sounded unusually cheerful. "Well, then, I think you'll like this. The yacht broker has a potential buyer for your boat."

Melissa wasn't surprised after Hunt's explosion. "You mean it's sold?"

"No, it's not that easy, I'm afraid. First, there are a couple of formalities to be taken care of. Have you got a pen?"

"Just a second." She dug out a crumpled provisions list to write on and a stub of pencil. "Yes."

"What you need to do is contact the yacht broker directly and he can fill you in on the details. His number is 774–2377."

"774–2377."

"Right. If everything goes smoothly, we may be able to wrap this up without too much delay. You know I've been hoping all along the boat would sell quickly so that you would come home. Give me a call next week and let me know how things are going. I'll be anxious to hear from you."

Melissa cleared the phone line, then plugged more change into the slot and punched in the number Morgan had given her.

"Caribbean Yachts," a feminine voice answered.

She explained who she was, then her call was transferred, and a second voice came on the line.

"Hello, Miss Catterly. My name is Brad Johnston. I'm so glad we get to speak at last. Did your lawyer give you any details about the deal we have pending?"

"No, Mr. Johnston. He didn't."

"Call me Brad, please. Well, basically, it comes down to this. My clients have seen the charter promotion video on *Whitecap* and are interested in a formal inspection and a demonstration sail. If the real thing matches the information they have, they're ready to buy. Cash deal, at your asking price. There's no question of their qualifications to purchase. I have a ten percent deposit check here in front of me and a letter of credit from their bank attesting to the availability of the balance. The wife loves the boat, which is the key to the whole thing. It's practically a done deal already. I expect we can complete the sale quite rapidly once the formalities are out of the way."

Melissa listened to his words. Daggers of regret stabbed at her heart. She was genuinely enjoying her new lifestyle, and now it was crashing to an end.

He went on. "They want to fly in and see the boat this weekend. When I couldn't get in touch with you I contacted your booking agent. He told me you had a cancellation this week, so I went ahead and set everything up for Saturday. Would that be any problem for you?"

Melissa hesitated. "No, no problem at all, Mr. Johnston, I mean, Brad," she said, trying to sound cheerful. "*Whitecap* will be ready and waiting."

She thought of Hunt. He wouldn't have wanted to be around for this sail, anyway. But she couldn't do it alone. She'd have to find someone else.

"Marvelous," Brad gushed. "We'll see you on Saturday morning then."

At noontime Friday, Melissa went to Langley's for a business lunch. As Erich had predicted, few charter captains were available at this time of the season. Those who were between jobs were looking for a permanent position and lost interest when she told them *Whitecap* might be sold. As of today, she was getting desperate and her requirements had changed. All she wanted now was someone to handle the demonstration sail. The charter for next week had also been cancelled, so all she hoped for was to get through tomorrow.

A dark-haired, middle-aged man with a ruddy complexion entered the restaurant, spoke to the bartender, and then sauntered to her table.

"Melissa Catterly?" he asked. He stood with his thumbs hooked on the pockets of a worn and faded pair of blue jeans.

"Yes, sit down, please. You must be Manny—"

"Sure am, little lady." He turned a chair backwards and sat with his arms leaning on the back. "The agency sent me over. Said you needed a captain."

"Would you like some lunch?" she offered.

He lit a cigarette and inhaled deeply. "I already got a beer comin', thanks." He tilted his head back and played with the smoke, forming small clouds with his lips.

Melissa winced inwardly. This man was not even

close to suitable for a charter boat captain. His rough edges and too-familiar manner would be offensive to any guest. But, she reminded herself, all he has to do is sail *Whitecap* for one day.

She sipped her iced tea, stared at the red and green parrot tattooed on his right arm, and then set down her glass. "I understand you've spent quite a bit of time in the islands and have—"

He interrupted her again. "Sure have, darlin'. Know these rocks like the back of my hand. And there isn't a sailboat around I can't set to flyin'."

"Let's get something straight right now, Mr. Puglesi. I am not your darlin' or little lady. My name is Melissa, and that's how I want to be addressed. What I need is someone to sail a boat tomorrow. The yacht broker and I will do all the talking and entertaining of our passengers. Your job will be to show off just what the boat can do. I've been told you can handle that. Is that true?"

He grinned at her and his eyes were insolent when he answered. "Yes, Ma'am."

She pushed back her chair and stood. "Be at the dock at seven A.M. sharp then. I'll pick you up there."

Chapter Twelve

The prior week's cancellation had been good for *Whitecap*. Before he quit, Hunt had spent the morning varnishing, and her brightwork shone in the tropical sunshine. Melissa had polished all the bronze, copper, and stainless steel and cleaned until even the bilges were spotless. With fresh flowers gracing each cabin, her monogrammed linens on display, and her deck and topsides scrubbed, she radiated the aura of a magnificent yacht.

Brad Johnston brought the Swensens aboard at nine o'clock. Mr. Swensen was a successful industrialist who liked to spend every weekend on the water. Mrs. Swensen hated the water, but loved her husband.

Mr. Swensen explained it to Melissa. "My darling wife indulges my fascination with the sea even though she's uneasy on boats. Therefore, I feel it's my duty to make sure that she has every possible luxury to surround her while she's aboard."

Melissa smiled politely. "I'm sure you'll find *Whitecap* an excellent choice."

After Brad spent an hour showing the Swensens through the boat, Melissa served a small brunch. She meticulously arranged the juice, fruit salad, aromatic coffee and fresh-baked croissants on the cockpit table to show off *Whitecap*'s china and crystal. The beauty of the islands around them and the impeccable condition of the vessel seemed to have put the couple in a fine mood. They chatted with Brad in the cockpit while Melissa cleared the dishes. As she came back on deck to remove the last water glasses, Mr. Swensen was telling Brad his impression.

"The vessel seems to be in excellent condition. If she sails as good as she looks, it appears our search for the perfect sailboat will be over."

After brunch, Manny and Melissa slipped *Whitecap*'s mooring and headed her out of the bay, ready for a pleasant sail. Melissa felt the fresh trade winds on her face and knew the conditions were perfect. She watched as *Whitecap* glided over the water merrily. Her bow split the waves and pushed them effortlessly aside. Her full complement of snow-white sails cast fleeting shadows on the clear seas as they raced by.

Passing Christmas Cove, with Manny at the helm, Melissa glanced at the boat's instruments. *Whitecap* was on a broad reach going ten knots in only nine feet of water. She did the math quickly. Only three feet of water separated the boat's deep keel from the seabed.

Alarm bells clanged in her head, but she tried to be tactful. "Don't you think we're a little too close to shore, Captain?"

As the warning left her mouth, Melissa heard the sickening impact. Mrs. Swensen screamed. They were all thrown violently forward. Throughout the boat, gear crashed to the floor. The fine bow dipped below the waves. The stern lifted clear of the water. A harsh, grating noise reverberated through the boat's interior and Melissa's soul. As *Whitecap*'s five-ton keel hit the solid rock of the reef, the fifteen tons of her hull, accommodations and equipment tried to continue in the direction of her previous motion.

The boat ground to a stop and Melissa regained her balance. She spun around and snapped at Manny. "I thought you said you knew these waters. You're totally incompetent. You ought to be ashamed to call yourself a captain!"

He glared at her with hatred in his eyes. Then he started the engine and slammed the gearshift into reverse.

For a few seconds she was unsure of what to do, then the consequences of running the boat aground started to seep into her mind. She looked to the Swensens. Mrs. Swensen was shaking and sobbing and rubbing her left shoulder. Melissa jumped up and went to her.

"Are you all right, Mrs. Swensen?"

The lady sobbed harder. "Yes. I think so."

Then Brad's voice came from below. "Miss Catterly," he called, "we're taking on water."

Melissa felt her entire body go cold as stone. Her stomach contracted spasmodically into a tight painful knot. She spun around and rushed below.

She stopped short and stared apprehensively into the deep bilge where Brad had lifted the floorboards. Several inches of unwelcome seawater swirled ominously before her eyes. Her ears told her that the automatic pump was already working.

She sensed there was no time to lose. "Brad, stay here and keep an eye on the water level. If the main pump can't handle it, activate the secondary. It's the bottom switch on the control panel." The many conversations she had listened to at Langley's helped her decide what to do next. "Brenton's Marine is in Crown Bay, isn't it?"

"Yes, it is," he confirmed.

"Let's hope we can get there," she called over her shoulder as she hurried back to the cockpit.

Manny still had *Whitecap* in reverse, trying to back her away from the reef. But the steady force of the wind on the sails continued to hold the large yacht firmly aground. When Melissa saw what was happening, she ripped at the lines that kept the sails taunt, releasing them out of their cleats.

She barked an order at him, her anxiety mixed with

anger. "Get away from the wheel, Manny. Go furl those sails."

As soon as the sails lost their influence, the boat started backward. Melissa took the wheel and slowly increased the power. With her jaw clenched tightly, she inched the big boat into deeper water, then turned the bow westward, away from the reef.

Brad Johnston came out through the companionway. "I've started the second pump."

Her heart skipped several beats. *Whitecap* would sink if the two pumps weren't enough.

I wish Hunt were here. He belongs here. Think! What should I do? What would Hunt do?

"Brad, take the wheel a minute."

Melissa rushed below to the engine room. Her hands shook as she knelt in the water and cut through the engine's water intake hose. She bit her lip and wedged the end into a position where it would suck seawater out of the bilge.

Then she dashed back to the cockpit, relieved Brad at the helm, and reached for the radio microphone.

On this Saturday afternoon, Hunt sat with the sparse crowd at Langley's. He ignored the sound of the VHF radio in the background. It was just noise that most sailors were accustomed to hearing. All day long it broadcast intermittent chatter, as the crew of one boat spoke to another crew or to someone ashore. It was the local party line. Every conversation was broadcast for all to overhear.

The familiar sound of Melissa's voice caught Hunt's attention immediately. He raised his head and strained to listen to her words through the noise.

Melissa was trying to contact Tom Brenton's boat-yard. "Brenton's Marine, Brenton's Marine, Brenton's Marine, this is *Whitecap*, KCX407."

The answer came. "*Whitecap*, this is Brenton's Marine, KFB772. Switch to channel seven two. Over."

Melissa disagreed. "Negative Brenton's Marine. This is an emergency. Please stay on channel sixteen, I don't want to lose you. Over."

"Yes. What can we do for you? Over."

The customers at Langley's knew that anyone who stayed on channel sixteen was in serious trouble. It was the international hailing and distress channel. Casual conversations broke off or trailed away to silence as everyone stopped to listen.

Melissa's voice came back. "We're in need of an emergency haul-out. We have struck a reef and are taking on water rapidly. I estimate we can be at your yard in twenty minutes, if our pumps can handle it. We're a sixty-five foot sailboat with six-foot draft. Can you pull the boat out immediately when we get there? Over."

Brenton's answered. "Yes, Ma'am. I understand the situation. We'll have the slipway clear and the lift waiting when you get here. Do you need any other assistance? Over."

"No, thank you," Melissa replied. "I'm going to

contact the Coast Guard. Just stand by if you would, please. Over."

"Will do," the marina voice replied. "Oh, and Ma'am . . . good luck. Over."

"Thank you," Melissa said. Then she ended the conversation, "This is *Whitecap*, KCX407, clear on sixteen."

"Brenton's Marine, KFB772, clear and standing by."

Hunt's attention was riveted to the radio as Melissa began another call. Her voice was clear and strong and he could picture how she would be holding her chin up slightly as she talked.

"Coast Guard St. Thomas, Coast Guard St. Thomas, Coast Guard St. Thomas, this is *Whitecap*, KCX407."

The Coastguardsman answered quickly. "This is Coast Guard St. Thomas, *Whitecap*. We monitored your previous transmission, Captain. Do you require assistance? Over."

Hunt heard Melissa's voice waver. "We're taking on a lot of water. I'm not sure we can make it to the boatyard. If necessary, I'll head her toward shore and beach her in shallow water. Right now, we have no one seriously injured, but we have five people onboard in danger. If you could have a boat intercept us in case we do need to take people off, we would feel more secure. Over."

"We'll get a boat started to rendezvous with you immediately. Please make sure that everyone onboard is wearing a life preserver, just in case. Anything else, Captain? Over."

"Yes," Melissa added, "please have them bring a high-capacity pump."

Hunt's mind was reeling as he listened to Melissa answering the Coastguardsman's questions concerning the type and size of boat and their precise location. Over and over again her words echoed in his mind. *"If our pumps can handle it." Pumps. Plural.* He knew exactly the capacity of each of *Whitecap*'s two pumps. He also knew the amount of water that she must be taking on for both pumps to be needed.

He hoped that Melissa would think of the fact that she could use the engine's water pump to help keep the boat afloat, then wondered who was on the boat with her. He sat bent over with his elbows resting on his knees, staring at the floor between his feet. *How could she have done this to* Whitecap? He gritted his teeth and the muscles in his jaw twitched. *So, here I sit, helpless to do anything for the boat I love, or the woman who's ripping apart my heart. Why couldn't she have stayed in North Carolina, where she belongs?*

Half an hour later, all the pumps were still working hard but managing to keep up with the relentless inflow. *We're almost there.* Melissa steered *Whitecap* into Crown Bay and spoke to her Coast Guard escort on the radio, thanking them for their support. Mrs.

Swensen, who had been weeping ever since the accident, saw the boatyard and collapsed into her husband's arms in relief. Melissa held her breath and guided the wide boat into the narrow slipway.

Immediately, the huge straps of the travel-lift tightened under *Whitecap*'s hull and lifted the boat safely clear of the water. Melissa winced as the boat was lifted up into the air. A solid stream of seawater poured out from the gaping space between her keel and hull. She saw four of the massive keel bolts stretched across the chasm, no longer securing the surfaces together.

She stood with her shoulders slumped viewing the damage. Her energy drained from her body like the water that gushed from *Whitecap*'s wound. When she saw Manny quietly pick up his backpack to leave, she couldn't even find the strength to upbraid him for his actions.

Brad Johnston stepped beside her. "The Swensens and I will be going now, Miss Catterly. I'm sure you can understand that they've lost all interest in purchasing *Whitecap*."

She nodded, hoping that the numbness she felt meant that this was all a nightmare.

Then Tom Brenton, the boatyard owner, said, "At first glance, it looks pretty serious, Miss Catterly. We won't know for sure just how serious until I make a closer inspection, of course. But from what I see right now, I can say for sure you're done chartering for the rest of this season."

* * *

For the next few hours, Melissa functioned much like an automaton. She made arrangements for a survey of *Whitecap*'s damage, then went on board to cover the furled sails. She picked up the pieces of the shattered juice glasses, scrubbed the sticky liquid from the floors, removed the withered daisies strewn on the main cabin sole, and swept up the soil spilled from an overturned pot of basil. She turned off all the navigation instruments and, with a trembling hand, made a terse but descriptive entry in the ship's log. With Tom Brenton's help, she switched the refrigerator and freezer over to the boatyard's electrical supply. Then, as the sun prepared to disappear behind the hills, she surveyed the boat's silent interior, checking for anything she might have overlooked.

She opened the door to the barrenness of Hunt's cabin. The lingering scent of his aftershave filled her with melancholy longing. She fled to her own cabin, gathered a change of clothing, and then climbed down the ladder to the ground. She retreated to an impersonal hotel room in Charlotte Amalie.

That night, in the lonely darkness, she cried for Hunt and the hurt she knew he would feel when he learned of the accident. She also wept for *Whitecap*.

Tom Brenton had a reputation for knowing his business well. His workmanship had earned him high esteem among the local charter crews, and they kept his yard busy all year long. It was Monday afternoon before he contacted Melissa to report his assessment of the damage. She stood in the boatyard and listened to his recommendations.

"You're very lucky, Miss Catterly. *Whitecap* is a well-built boat and the damage isn't too extensive. There are a lot of boats around that would have had the keel ripped right off and sunk on the spot. Your boat can most certainly be repaired as good as new. But, unfortunately, my schedule is packed. I won't be able to work on her for quite some time."

"How long will it be?"

"A few weeks minimum. Most likely you're looking at five weeks before we can start work and then a full week to complete it. An estimator from your insurance company was here this morning, so at least the expense shouldn't be a problem."

Melissa reviewed *Whitecap*'s charter reservations in her mind. The last couple weeks of the season, the only slots that hadn't been booked yet, would be the only time when the boat would be seaworthy again.

She sighed heavily. "I was hoping you could get to it sooner. My insurance policy only covers the damage. It won't make up for lost business."

"I'm sorry. I'd like to help you, but there's nothing I can do."

Melissa thanked Tom and he left. She climbed the tall ladder and went aboard *Whitecap*.

She sat in the cockpit sorting out her thoughts. There would be customers to be notified and refunds to be issued. Roger would have to handle those business matters. The more worrisome issue was her finances. She had nowhere to live but a costly hotel. Somehow she would have to shoulder the burden of the uninsured expenses. She thought, with a stab of regret, that there was one expense she didn't have: a captain's salary.

She realized there wasn't much more she could do here and that finding another buyer for *Whitecap* would probably be impossible while the damage was being repaired. She decided to inquire at the airlines about flights back to Wilmington.

She glanced out across the bay and remembered the carefree day with Hunt at the tiny hidden beach. It would be the perfect place to formulate a plan. She would pack her things and finish closing up the boat tomorrow.

The boat seemed barren and still. Not at all the vibrant home she knew. Somberly, she tiptoed to her cabin and found the white bikini she had bought the day before leaving Wilmington. She wondered what could have possessed her that day that would have made her buy such a revealing suit. Was it possible that, even then, she was attracted to Hunt? She forcefully stopped herself from speculating, and grabbed some sunscreen, and a couple oversized beach towels. Then she walked to Brenton's dock, climbed aboard *Whitecap*'s tender, and sped away.

The noontime sun was characteristically hot as Hunt guided his borrowed runabout to the small dock at

Brenton's. After the lines were secure, he walked up the incline to where *Whitecap* sat. Before leaving for his new job on John Myers' dive boat, he wanted to see the damage for himself. He stood in the small patch of shade cast by her hull, staring at the wound to her underbody. After a few minutes, he moved in closer. Running his fingers gently over the bent bolts and cracked fiberglass, he made his own assessment of what it would take to heal his friend.

As he examined the injured hull he couldn't help but think of Melissa. *She's quite a lady,* he concluded. He knew this damage could have been catastrophic for the boat if she hadn't reacted quickly and kept her composure. He admired her tenacity and how she'd handled herself and gotten *Whitecap* to safety.

Tom Brenton was on his way to the dock and saw him beside the boat. "Hunt, isn't it? I know we've met before but my memory is terrible, I can't remember where."

Hunt extended his hand. "Hunt Stewart." He nodded his head toward *Whitecap*. "I was her captain until a week ago. You did some rigging work for us two years ago."

"Now, I remember." Tom smiled. "You were the typical doting parent, sticking your nose into everything we did."

Hunt laughed. "That was me, all right." He looked toward the sailboat and the smile left his face. "Looks like she'll survive with some TLC."

"Oh sure, she'll be okay eventually. But I'm

jammed up with work right now. She's going to be out of commission for at least six weeks."

Hunt whistled a low exclamation. "That's quite a blow to any charter boat. Lots of refunds. And from what I heard the prospective buyers flew the coop, pronto."

"Yeah. Miss Catterly took it all pretty hard. She doesn't seem to care very much about losing the sale. But like any boat lover she's hurting for a fine vessel."

Hunt narrowed his eyes in a confused frown. *She is? She's hurting for* Whitecap?

"Speaking of Melissa, do you know where she's staying?" Hunt asked Tom as he started to leave. The question slipped out, and he was surprised at his own words.

Tom gave him a wave. "At the Sea Horse Cottages. But you probably won't find her there for a while. She was here this morning. One of the yardmen saw her leaving in her tender about an hour ago. Normally they don't notice people come and go, but I guess she was wearing a pretty eye-catching bikini."

After Tom left, Hunt mused over the conversation. *Did I misjudge her feelings for* Whitecap? *Did the boat mean more to her than just money? Sure I was hurt, but I shouldn't have walked out on Missy. Maybe I should have let her explain. I'm starting to regret a lot about the day I quit.*

Hunt had planned to stop at the boatyard and then head for Langley's. Now, instead of returning to Red

Hook, he pointed the bow of the runabout toward the tiny private beach where he suspected Melissa might be. The more he thought about her, the more he wanted to see her.

Chapter Thirteen

Melissa rolled onto her stomach and the hot, after-noon sun began to soak into the muscles of her back. She spread the fingers of her left hand, looked at her ring finger, and thought about Morgan's proposal. *If I'd stayed with Morgan to begin with I could have avoided all this. I could have been insulated from all these problems with* Whitecap. *He would have handled everything.* She released a slow sigh. *But then I would have missed so much. I never would have known Hunt.*

The thought of Hunt sent a cloud of despair over her and she stood and walked to the edge of the spar-kling water. *Is it better this way? Was I getting too attached? Was I leaving myself open to getting hurt even worse? I need to learn from the past.* She drifted into memories of the intoxicating feel of his lips.

The sound of an outboard motor disturbed her solitude. She scanned the horizon, looking for the source. The offending noise grew louder, and she shaded her eyes to watch as a small black boat approached, threatening to ruin the solitude of her private beach. Then she recognized the driver.

For half a second she thought that it was just wishful thinking. Although she hadn't seen him since he quit, his face kept appearing in her mind. Every time she closed her eyes she remembered his twinkling eyes and quick wit. But then the boat came closer, and more primitive senses inside her told her that it was really Hunt.

A mixture of joy and regret washed over her. She knew she should have told him everything from the start. Then neither of them, and certainly not *Whitecap*, would be in the unpleasant positions they were in today. She decided that she needed to apologize to Hunt. But she wasn't sure he would forgive her.

As Hunt approached the beach, the engine stopped. She stood motionless and watched the runabout's momentum carry it to shore. Then he stepped over the side into the shallow aquamarine water and pulled the boat up onto the sand.

She was tongue-tied. Her chest ached and her mouth went dry. Her heartbeat started to race and she fought back an almost irresistible urge to run to him.

He turned toward Melissa and for a fleeting moment, their eyes locked. Then she heard the smooth notes of his voice. "I thought you might be here."

Happiness exploded through her. "Were you looking for me?"

"I wanted to talk to you . . . about *Whitecap*."

"Whitecap?" She didn't care that her voice oozed sarcasm. "Of course, I should have guessed, *Whitecap*."

"Don't get defensive. I'm not blaming you."

She planted her fists on her hips. "Well, how nice of you. Who are you blaming?"

"That idiot you hired, for one."

"You didn't leave me much choice. I needed a captain."

"A captain? Does that guy even have a license? I could have found a Boy Scout more qualified."

Her voice rose. "Well, you didn't. You deserted, remember?"

"And whose fault was that? Who didn't have the consideration to tell me she was selling my boat?"

"Your boat? *Whitecap* is *my* boat. I can sell her. I can hire whoever I want for a captain. I don't have to get your permission or explain myself to you."

"Oh, I assure you, it's quite clear to me that she's yours. But you don't deserve to own her. Not unless you understand that a boat isn't something you buy and sell like a sack of potatoes. A boat's like a person, a friend."

She narrowed her eyes and practically spat the words, "Or a mistress?"

"Sure, why not a mistress? One female in a man's life who isn't demanding or jealous."

"Jealous! You think I'm jealous? Of a boat?"

"That isn't what I said." But he smiled mockingly.

She sputtered. "Well, good. Because I'm not." But inside she was shocked to realize that she was. She shook her head and swung her hair backward over her shoulders, then lifted her chin. "You want to live for that boat? Fine. I certainly don't care."

He took a step closer until they were almost touching, close enough that she could smell the masculine scent that always wiped everything else from her mind. "Missy, please, let's not argue. That's not why I'm here."

"Why did you come?"

He took her face between his hands and looked into her eyes. "I had to see you," he whispered. "I can't just let you walk out of my life."

She knew what he was going to do. At a rational level, she didn't want it to happen. Yet, at every other level, she knew she did.

He bent and tenderly kissed her. She felt his hands sliding down her neck and over the smooth, bare skin of her shoulders. She pressed her lips against his in reply.

She held her breath as he placed more light kisses across her cheek and along the line of her jaw. Then she spoke, still so close to him that her lips brushed his face. "I'm sorry, Hunt. I was wrong. Don't be angry with me."

He stroked her hair and rested his cheek against her brow. "Do I seem angry?"

"No. Not right now. But you were a few minutes ago and the other day."

"That's history. We both made mistakes. I should never have walked out on you like that."

"Are we . . . friends again?"

"Yes, . . . friends."

For several minutes they stood together on the beach. Then Hunt dropped his arm and took her hand in his and they walked to the towel she had spread out on the sand. They sat quietly only inches apart. Hunt closed his eyes and tilted his face toward the sun. Melissa tried to sort out her confused thoughts, but she couldn't. They were spinning too chaotically, like tiny grains of sand caught up in wildly breaking surf.

Melissa remained silent, wanting to prolong the magic spell. Since his arrival, the day seemed brighter, the birds happier, and the breeze gentler. She smelled the heady perfume of the flowers and was enchanted to see all the blues of the spectrum shimmering in the sea.

Time seemed nonexistent until Hunt asked, "Hey, you know something, I didn't have any lunch and I'm starved. Did you bring any food?"

"No, I guess you're going to have to shinny up a coconut tree."

He jumped to his feet. "Oh, no, I won't. Be right back."

A few minutes later, he stumbled back to the beach, his arms loaded with ripe mangoes and his feet scratched from climbing the tree limbs covered with rough bark. The fruit tasted delicious, and they ate several, until they had juice running down their chins and their hands were sticky with the sweet nectar.

They washed in the ocean then Hunt stood and looked at her intently. "Why didn't you tell me you owned *Whitecap*?"

Melissa sighed. "At first it was because Mr. Barnes's son was contesting the will. My lawyer told me not to even go near the boat, let alone tell you who I was. Later, after his son dropped his claim, I didn't want to upset our professional relationship. You're an excellent captain, and I didn't want to influence you. Actually, I felt more like you owned her, until the day you quit." She looked into his eyes, searching for understanding. "I'm sorry, Hunt. You have every right to be upset."

He took her hand and held it in his. "I overreacted. I couldn't believe that you'd sell *Whitecap*. I just went into shock when Roger told me." He paused for a minute. "Listen, Missy, we've got to do something about *Whitecap*. That was part of the reason I came out here to find you. We can't just leave her sitting in a boatyard."

"I hate that thought, too," Melissa agreed. "But what else can we do?"

Hunt grinned. "Well, if you really want to get her back in the water, I have an idea."

"What kind of an idea?"

"Let's jury rig a patch on her keel and take her over

to Puerto Rico. I have a good friend, Luis, who owns a boatyard in Fajardo and owes me a favor. He's a wizard with fiberglass. I'm sure he'll do a great job, and fast enough that we can salvage at least part of the season."

"Where's Fajardo?"

"On Puerto Rico's eastern coast. Roger and I were stationed near there, at Roosevelt Roads, in our Navy days. It's about four hours downwind from Brenton's. If we can stop the water from coming in, we shouldn't have any problem getting there."

Melissa only had to think for a second. Hunt loved *Whitecap* and wouldn't attempt a trip to Puerto Rico unless they could make it. And if they could get *Whitecap* repaired and save part of the season, then they should try.

"If you think it'll work, that's good enough for me. Let's do it," she told him.

Hunt smiled widely. "We'll go over there and figure out how to put a patch on her in the morning."

The day's heat moderated as the sun began to slip lower in the sky. Together, they sat on the beach and watched the fiery sunset, then the birth of a million stars.

Morning sunlight streamed through the windows of her hotel room as Melissa dressed quickly, slipping on a Mickey Mouse T-shirt and her cut-off jeans. She hummed the melody of a Strauss waltz as she plaited her hair into one long braid and draped it to one side.

Hunt would be at the hotel to pick her up in ten minutes and they were due at the boatyard in half an hour.

She checked out of her room and went outside to wait in front of the hotel, smiling in anticipation of getting back aboard *Whitecap*. She yawned, feeling exhausted from the last three days' work of helping Hunt put a patch in place over the boat's damaged keel. She had sanded the surrounding fiberglass to insure a good bond and then, using epoxy and fiberglass cloth, he had applied a bandage-like covering sealed at the edges. When they were done, the finished product had looked crude and ugly to her, but he seemed confident it would work. Today would be the test of his efforts. *Whitecap* was going back into the water.

An island taxi screeched to a halt and Melissa climbed in. Hunt brushed his lips softly over hers. The cab driver's eyes appeared in the rearview mirror. He turned up the volume on the already blaring radio and, with a screech of tires, roared back out onto the road.

Tom Brenton fully cooperated with Hunt's plan. It was what he would probably do himself, he told Melissa, and agreed to make time in his tight schedule to launch the boat.

As their taxi drew up to the boatyard entrance, Melissa saw *Whitecap* already hanging in midair, suspended over the water. She held her breath and crossed her fingers as Tom slowly lowered the yacht until she was floating at her waterline.

Immediately, Hunt jumped aboard and went below to check for leaks. A few minutes later he came back on deck, beaming.

"She's holding, the bilge is dry as a bone," he announced to Melissa and Tom. "Looks like we're in business."

Melissa saw the joy on his face and, once again, she empathized with his feelings for *Whitecap*. It was the kind of bond that she had only seen before between a man and a special friend or a beloved pet, except that this was a completely one-sided affection.

Tom finished the launching, removing the massive straps from around the hull and then backing the travel-lift from the slipway.

Hunt was whistling as he prepared the rigging for the sail to Fajardo. Every few minutes he ducked below. Each time he returned smiling.

Even though the trade winds were not as boisterous as usual, Melissa sat on the edge of her seat for the entire sail to Puerto Rico. Every wind gust that heeled *Whitecap* caused her pulse to race. Every wave slap plucked at her taunt nerves. Hunt continued his frequent inspection trips to the bilge until she was sure his legs must feel as if they were made of lead from climbing up and down the companionway ladder. When, finally, four hours later they circled around Isleta Marina and into the harbor in Fajardo, she longed for the chance to sleep for a week.

Luis met Hunt and Melissa at the slipway and embraced Hunt warmly. Melissa watched and listened as they had a lively conversation in a combination of half Spanish and half English. Then Hunt slipped his arm around her waist and introduced her to his friend.

"Hunt, you did not tell me on the phone that you were bringing a señorita of such beauty," Luis chastised him. "This changes things, of course. Your pretty lady can not stay in this pitiful town. You must take my home in the mountains while you are here." He winked at Melissa and his mouth turned up in a toothy grin. "Mi casa es muy romántico, and the nights, they are cool. You may even have to cuddle to stay warm. You can relax and forget all your troubles. Allow me to call the housekeeper and see that she has everything ready for you."

Hunt started to protest but Luis was adamant.

He took them to his home in town and his wife served them a delectable meal of traditional paella. Then he gave them the keys to his car and sent them away to his coffee plantation in Adjuntas, promising them, "Do not worry about your boat, my friends. I will begin the work on her mañana. Early in the morning."

To Melissa it was a dreamland. She walked through the house and grounds feeling like a fairy princess. The estate was high in the western Puerto Rican mountains where the climate suited coffee cultivation well. The altitude made the nights cool even in summer and coffee had thrived here for hundreds of years.

The main house was built with a profusion of bal-conies and wrought-iron grillwork and enclosed a large central courtyard. There, magnificent plants and flowers were interspersed with small benches, and a miniature fountain cooled the air. In her mind's eye Melissa pictured dashing Spanish conquistadors and shy, chaperoned señoritas strolling among the feathery ferns.

Standing on the balcony, Melissa looked out over the nearby hills, which were white with fragrant coffee blossoms basking in the dappled sunshine. As the housekeeper helped Melissa unpack, she explained that soon the bushes would be red with seed-bearing coffee "cherries". And they would become the green coffee beans.

For two days they watched sunsets from the balcony and walked in the gardens. Hunt tinkered with the pro-jects awaiting repair in the handyman's shop, and Mel-issa experimented with cooking the foods the housekeeper kept stored in the pantry.

The second afternoon Hunt sliced open his finger. He came into the kitchen sheepishly holding a bloody cloth around his hand. "Have you run across a bandage anywhere around here?" he asked Melissa.

"Hunt! What did you do?"

"Cut myself on a broken lawnmower I was trying to repair." He showed her his finger.

"I think you'll live. It's almost stopped bleeding. Come over here and wash it out in the sink." She took his hand, positioned it under the running water, and told him, "Stay here a minute."

She left the room. A minute later, she returned with a bottle of hydrogen peroxide, took his hand from the water, and dried it with some clean gauze squares. Then she saturated another square with the disinfectant and bathed his wound.

"You do that very well," he said.

She looked at him from the corner of her eye. "I suppose next you're going to ask me to kiss it and make it better."

A grin flashed across his face. "Sounds good to me."

She rolled her eyes and smiled.

"Seriously, Missy, you're a regular Florence Nightingale. Where did you learn so much about this stuff?"

She paused for a few seconds then said, barely in a whisper, "When I was growing up my mother was constantly in and out of hospitals. For a while I thought I wanted to be a nurse."

"What changed your mind?"

"My brother had a skydiving accident when I was eighteen. He was in an intensive care unit for two weeks before he died. When I saw all the suffering the nurses had to deal with, I knew that nursing wouldn't be a good career for me. I couldn't bear to work in those kinds of surroundings."

"So you became a chef?"

"Yes. I've always loved to cook. So after college, I decided to go to Bambridge's and learn the skills I needed to tackle gourmet meals." She took a deep breath, let it out quickly, and went on. "It's ironic, you know. I didn't want to see people suffer. To shield myself from that I became a chef. Then, later, I took the job working for Mr. Barnes. And opened myself up to the hurt of watching him die a slow, painful death."

She hung her head, and a single tear wet her cheek.

He pulled her close and rested her head on his shoulder, tenderly stroking her hair. "Don't think about it any more," he murmured. "It's okay now. If I have anything to say about it, nothing will ever hurt you again."

Chapter Fourteen

The evening turned chilly and Hunt lit a roaring fire in the drafty old manor house. Melissa prepared their meal of a fresh garden salad, chicken basted with orange-raisin sauce, sweet potato soufflé, and baby sweet peas and served it on a low table in the cozy firelight of the warm living room. They sat on thick cushions to eat. Afterward, they lounged near the hearth.

Melissa fidgeted with the carpet nap. She knew they needed to discuss *Whitecap*. Her conversations with Hunt in the last few days hadn't included any mention of the future. She had to tell him that the accident made her situation even worse and that she still must sell the boat. But she didn't know how to broach the subject.

She felt him kiss the top of her head. Then he put his finger under her chin and raised her lips to his.

Her mind overflowed with confusion as she savored the sensation of his feathery kiss. When he drew away she opened her eyes and met his. She worried that he might leave her again when she said what she had to say. She searched his face for a clue, then she summoned all her courage.

"Hunt, I think we need to talk," she said quietly.

"Sure. What did you want to talk about?"

She couldn't think of any way to soften the words. "It's about *Whitecap*. I still don't have any choice but to sell her, you know."

Hunt straightened up and stared into the leaping flames of the crackling fire. The orange glow made his frown seem ominous to her. "Why?"

Melissa's words tumbled out of her mouth like water from a dam suddenly broken. "What it all comes down to is that I don't have the money to keep her. Everything would be fine if I could be sure she'd have a good season every year. If that was the case, she would always pay for her own maintenance, and . . . the expenses like your salary. But, if she has a bad season again, like last year, and I can't salvage much from this year, somebody has to make up the difference. I don't have the kind of money it takes to offset a large loss. I'd have to go into debt. Eventually, I'd lose her anyway, except to pay off my creditors. I wish there was some way to keep her, too, but I can't."

"What if you didn't have those expenses, Missy? Would you keep her then?"

Melissa answered without hesitation. "Of course, I would. She's a wonderful boat, Hunt. I really enjoy sailing and living and working aboard her. I feel like a traitor putting her up for sale, especially considering Mr. Barnes wanted me to have her. Unfortunately, what I want doesn't change anything. The expenses aren't going to vanish into thin air."

"I know," he said. "But *Whitecap* can be a very profitable boat if you'll give her a chance. I'm sure of that. So sure, in fact, that I'll tell you what I'll do. It's a little late this year, but starting right now, suppose I don't take a salary during the season. Instead, you put the money into a bank account until the end of May. If it turns out that *Whitecap* has a good season and makes a profit, I'll get my entire salary plus interest and maybe a bonus based on a percentage of the profits. If you have a loss, you'll take whatever's needed to cover it out of the bank account. Whatever's left over, I'll get. I have some money saved that I was planning to use to buy *Whitecap* someday, and I can pay my personal expenses from that. So, what do you think?"

She furrowed her brow in a frown. Maybe it would be a good business arrangement for her. "That doesn't sound like it would be fair to you."

He smiled. "I guess I have more faith in *Whitecap*'s abilities than you do. The bad season last year was a fluke, not a trend. The charter business is like any other tourist industry. When the economy is depressed, people don't spend their money. Usually it works out that if the U.S. economy is slow we get more European guests. Last year, it just so happened that things were tough worldwide. This year's bookings are showing that the economy is swinging the other way though, and the industry is rebounding. You're going to see business getting even better in the next few years. I'll be getting great bonuses in the future. Why not try it? What have you got to lose?"

She stared at the pattern on the carpet without really seeing it. When Morgan had talked her into selling *Whitecap*, he had insisted that crew salaries would bankrupt her quickly. And the financial statements he'd sent her seemed to back that up. But if Hunt worked without a salary and she was the crew, that argument was invalid.

The problem with the arrangement was personal. She knew deep in her heart that she would do everything possible to keep their relationship smooth. But if he pressed her for more or turned away from her and became involved with another woman, she wouldn't be able to bear to see him every day. She knew she never wanted to hurt him again by separating him from the boat. She would have to be the one to leave. And someone else would have to be paid to take her place.

If Hunt was right about *Whitecap*'s potential profit, maybe she could afford to do that. And, if it didn't work out, as difficult as it would be for both of them, she could put the boat back on the market as a last resort.

For now, I can be with him.

A smile pulled at the corners of her mouth. "What have I got to lose? Nothing, I guess. That kind of an arrangement could make it possible for me to keep her."

Hunt's face lit up. "Well then, it's all settled. For this season, I'll contribute some of my savings if you need it. There's a chance this year may be better than you think, especially if Luis works fast. You know, we could start a whole new fad in the business world, kind of an extension of profit sharing. We can call it loss sharing. I doubt if it's an idea that would go over big with the brass at General Motors though."

"Probably not." Melissa laughed. Seeing him so obviously happy made her cheerful, too. She felt as if a tremendous burden had been lifted from her shoulders. She would keep *Whitecap*. She didn't have to worry about Mr. Barnes's boat in the hands of strangers, or of Hunt being separated from his special friend.

She thought of how different her new relationship with Hunt was from their initial captain and crew arrangement and experienced a subtle unease about the future. "I'll call Morgan in the morning and ask him to draw up a contract to protect your interests."

Hunt got up and moved toward the fire. He used the long poker to prod and group the glowing logs. The fire flared and a wave of white heat warmed her face. Then, he squared his shoulders and walked back to her. His face was creased in seriousness as he sat down at her side. "Tell me about Morgan Black."

"He was Mr. Barnes's attorney."

"I know that much. And I have the impression he's not fond of *Whitecap*. The return address on all those letters wasn't a law office. What about you and him?"

She squeezed her hands together in her lap. "We met while I worked for Mr. Barnes. We dated for a while."

"Seriously?"

"He asked me to marry him."

"And you said?"

"That I needed time to get over Mr. Barnes's death. That I needed time to think."

She saw his Adam's apple rise and fall before he asked, "Are you going to marry him?"

She glanced at his face. "No. But he's a kind, generous person."

Hunt fell silent. A flaming log popped and a drop of sap sizzled. She could see the muscles in his jaw clenching. A bead of perspiration formed at his brow. "I don't think he's going to like our business arrangement."

"Probably not. He's advised me all along to sell."

"What about you working on the boat with me? Is he trying to get you to give that up too?"

She squirmed, then raised her chin slightly higher. "Yes. But I make my own decisions about where I live and what I do."

"What about me, Missy?"

She met his gaze. "I don't know. You've complicated my mind."

"Missy, I love you. Stay here with me, marry me," he whispered.

She closed her eyes, feeling the wild pounding in her chest. Her pulse was racing. *Marriage needs to last forever.* A cautious, "You hardly know me," came from her lips.

He smiled. "I know the tunes you hum while you're kneading bread dough and what poetry you recite to your plants. Unless you have any other important secrets, like owning *Whitecap*, that's enough for me. We'll have years to learn the rest."

"That's not much to base a marriage on. I know almost nothing about your childhood. You don't know any of my bad habits. Maybe we're not compatible."

"Sure we are. We both want *Whitecap*; we both enjoy the ocean. You love to cook; I love to eat. I can even learn to tolerate yogurt, maybe."

He turned her hand over and put a warm, feather-light kiss on her palm. "Say yes, Missy. We can get married at the end of the season and have a couple weeks to be together on *Whitecap*, all by ourselves, when we go north."

Melissa placed her hand on his and searched his face for something to tell her what to do. She took a deep breath and smelled her own fear. If only she could be sure.

"I don't know. You've muddled my brain. I never expected this."

The dancing flames of the firelight lit the darkened room. Sap-filled pine logs crackled as they burned. The even rhythm of his breathing and the slightly rough texture of his hand filled her senses.

It took a minute for her to summon the courage to speak. "Hunt?"

"Yes."

"If we were to get married, someday I'd like to have children."

He drew in a deep breath. "I've thought about that."

"You have?"

"Quite a bit actually."

"Do you want that?"

She held her breath.

He ran his thumb along her chin and said softly, "Yes, I do."

Her eyes searched his. "But that would mean . . ."

"—that we'd have to buy a house somewhere on the water and move off *Whitecap*."

"Can you do that?"

"I love you. You're more important than anything else in the world to me." He raised his hand to gently capture hers and turned to kiss her fingertips. "I can't live without you, Missy. Unless you're beside me, there isn't any beauty in the sea or excitement in the wind. It's all worthless unless you'll share it with me."

"But—"

He put his finger across her lips to silence her protest. "Let me finish."

She nodded.

"I'll never want to be completely away from the sea. But when we're ready to have children, we'll compromise. We'll give them the best of both worlds. They'll have a stable home ashore with school and friends and piano lessons. But they'll also have vacations and summers filled with sailing and swimming and living in the fresh air. Being here in the mountains, I've realized that I can be happy with you anywhere."

Her fingers swept across his brow. "I love the way you look standing at the helm with the wind tousling your hair. I can't imagine you anywhere else."

"Until a few months ago, I never thought I'd *be* anywhere else. I never thought I'd want a wife or children. I thought the ocean was enough for me. But since I've met you, I know it's not. I've changed. I've fallen in love."

They sat communicating wordlessly for several minutes before either of them spoke.

Then Melissa smiled and tears of joy filled her eyes. "Yes, Hunt. I love you, too. I want to and I will marry you. Yes, yes, yes."

For less than a heartbeat, she hesitated. Then, she slid her arms around him. She pressed her face against his chest, drinking in the familiar scent of his aftershave. His embrace felt wonderful, even though it was so tight that she wondered if he might crush her bones.

They kissed. A kiss that was long and gentle and freed the emotions that could be shared only with each other.

* * *

Six weeks later, there was a small wedding onboard John Myers' motoryacht, *Mockingbird II*, in Newport Harbor. Roger was best man and Vivien Myers was matron of honor. The yacht was decorated brightly for the occasion. Along the side decks, a profusion of potted chrysanthemums, daffodils and violets bent merrily in the wind.

Hunt's parents and sister arrived on the dock just minutes before the ceremony. He led them to seats on the wide aft deck. Then, he turned toward the doorway expectantly as the joyous notes of an organ filled the air.

The bride wore a floor-length gown of white satin with long, Irish-lace sleeves and a sweeping train that was borrowed from her matron of honor. Her black hair was swept into a smooth coil at the top of her head and a small beaded tiara rested upon it, with a full veil bursting from the sides. Her ballet slippers left no marks on the deck. Her bouquet was of yellow, red and pink roses surrounded by white carnations. Around her neck hung a delicate silver chain supporting a tiny filigreed pendant. And on her face a radiant smile reflected his joy as she walked to stand by his side.

A gentle spring breeze blew across the harbor, and nearby, *Whitecap* waited. Gay multi-colored streamers flew from her rigging and garlands trimmed her decks and masts. Emblazoned across her stern was a large banner painted by Hunt:

DIAN G. SMITH

AMERICAN FILMMAKERS TODAY

Illustrated with Photographs

Woody Allen, Robert Altman, Mel Brooks, Francis Ford Coppola, Brian de Palma, George Lucas, Paul Mazursky, Martin Scorsese, and Steven Spielberg are creative filmmakers whose box office successes have earned them the privilege of making films the way they want.

This lively book is filled with quotes from actors and critics and fascinating analyses by the profiled moviemen themselves. It tells the stories of their early successes and failures, where they get their ideas, how they express their personalities in their work, and how they work with actors and actresses, and includes memorable scenes from their greatest films. *American Filmmakers Today* is an exciting glimpse behind the scenes of Hollywood and into the private and professional lives of the people who have entertained millions with such smash hits as *Star Wars, The Godfather, E.T.,* and *Annie Hall.*

AMERICAN

★ FILMMAKERS
TODAY

Dian G. Smith

JULIAN MESSNER
NEW YORK

All rights reserved including the right of
reproduction in whole or in part in any form.
Published by Julian Messner.
A Division of Simon & Schuster, Inc.
Simon & Schuster Building,
1230 Avenue of the Americas,
New York, New York 10020.
JULIAN MESSNER and colophon are trademarks of
Simon & Schuster, Inc.

Designed by Prairie Graphics

Manufactured in the United States of America

Library of Congress Cataloging in Publication Data.

Smith, Dian G.
    American filmmakers today.

    Bibliography: p.
    Includes index.
    1. Moving-picture producers and directors—United States—Biography.
I. Title.
PN1998.A2S567   1983   791.43'0233'0922   83-42785

ISBN: 0-671-44081-0

Acknowledgments

I am very grateful for the excellent film study collections of the Library of the Performing Arts (the New York Public Library at Lincoln Center) and the Museum of Modern Art in New York City, and for the great research library of Columbia University.

At Julian Messner, I would like to thank my editor, Jane Steltenpohl, who launched me on this project and provided wise criticism and guidance.

I must also thank Robert S. Smith, supporter, critic, and movie companion; Benjamin Eli and Emlen Matthew Smith, experts on *Star Wars*; and Marie-Nicole Exantus, the most skilled and loving baby-sitter.

ALSO BY DIAN G. SMITH
Careers in the Visual Arts
Talking with Professionals

Contents

Introduction

IN THE HEYDAY of Hollywood, directors (like actors) were hired hands, working under contract for one or another of the six major studios. They were kept busy churning out pictures to be shown on double bills in the studios' theater chains. Today the situation in Hollywood is very different.

The change began in 1948, when the Supreme Court ruled, under the antitrust laws, that the connection between the studios and the theaters was a monopoly. During the 1950s the studios were forced to sell their theaters. Without these guaranteed outlets, the risk in financing and producing films greatly increased (the average Hollywood movie today costs $10 million). At the same time, television was drawing audiences away, and the new suburban life-style was keeping families more often together at home. The studios had to cut back and began to rely on independent production companies to make many of their films, which they would then only distribute.

What this has meant for directors, in part, is a loss of security. But it has also meant, for some, the opportunity to do more than direct a film, to become what is often called a "filmmaker." A filmmaker has control over the film from conception through release—originating the idea, writing the screenplay, and then directing, producing, and perhaps acting in and marketing the film (or some influential combination of these).

The nine directors whose stories are told in this book took that opportunity. They are filmmakers who have used their total control to convey some vision of their own, to make personal films. Yet they walk a fine line between art and commerce. They were granted control of their films primarily because they can attract long enough lines to the box office to satisfy the studios.

A number of other filmmakers might have been included in this book—Hal Ashby, John Cassavetes, Terrence Malick, and Michael Ritchie, for instance. And among those chosen, some might consider George Lucas's films too commercial or Robert Altman's too personal. The intent was to find directors whose stated aim is to make personal films, who made their major films in the 1970s, and who seem likely to be making more in the 1980s. Ultimately, of course, any selection is a matter of personal judgment.

This book is limited to Hollywood directors because Hollywood films are the ones that most people see. In this country there is also a thriving underground of personal filmmakers whose films are distributed independently. They are sometimes bought by studios, but more often are distributed through less commercial outlets (art theaters, universities, museums, festivals).

The future for personal filmmakers in America is hard to predict, for the 1980s, like the 1950s, promise to be years of change in Hollywood. Cable TV, videocassettes, and other new technologies could provide a huge, hungry market for films. If so, a book on this subject published ten years from now might have twice as many names, including, one hopes, those of some women and some blacks.

Woody Allen

Take the Money and Run (1969)
Bananas (1971)
*Everything You Always Wanted
to Know about Sex* (1972)
Sleeper (1973)
Love and Death (1975)
Annie Hall (1977)
Interiors (1978)
Manhattan (1979)
Stardust Memories (1980)
A Midsummer Night's Sex Comedy (1982)
Zelig (1983)

WHO IS WOODY ALLEN? Is he the brainy nebbish of the nightclub acts and the early films, panting after women and terrorized by anything mechanical? Or is he Sandy Bates of *Stardust Memories*, the tormented filmmaker whose boorish fans won't allow him to express his concerns in serious films? Or is he someone else entirely?

In the first place, Woody Allen was not always Woody Allen. He was born Allen Stewart Konigsberg on December 1, 1935, in Flatbush, a lower-middle-class neighborhood in Brooklyn. And contrary to his weakling image, his father claims that he was

1

Woody Allen directing A *Midsummer Night's Sex Comedy*.

dubbed Woody by the kids on the block because he was always the one to bring the stick out for the stickball game. Woody also trained to be a featherweight fighter and would have entered the Golden Gloves if his father hadn't refused to sign the papers for him.

Woody's parents were poor, and when he was young they often lived with relatives because of the wartime housing shortage. His father held various jobs while Woody was growing up, including taxi driver and waiter, until he opened his own business as a jewelry engraver. His mother was a bookkeeper in a florist shop.

Woody and his younger sister Letty were raised as Orthodox Jews, and he went to Hebrew school for eight years. He isn't religious now, though, and was less than reverent even then. His father told an interviewer that at his bar mitzvah Woody put on blackface and did Al Jolson's jazz singer routine.

Although he made his parents the butt of some of his jokes ("Their values in life are God and carpeting," he used to say on the stage), he is actually fond of them and visits them regularly. And Letty is always one of the early viewers of his films.

As a child, Woody was shy and not very popular. He made fun of the bullying he suffered then in a nightclub joke about his stay at an interfaith camp: "I was sadistically beaten by boys of all races and creeds."

In general, Allen has described his childhood as "classic low-brow." He spent his time playing ball, watching wrestling on television, and reading comic books and Mickey Spillane novels. He also went to the Flatbush Theater five times a week, where he saw "vaudeville and movies and . . . every comic, every tap dancer, every magician, every kind of singer. . . . I could do everybody's act. I used to tear up the Raisinets boxes and write jokes down."

At the age of seven he saw Bob Hope in *The Road to Monaco* and decided that he wanted to be a comedian. Hope has remained an idol. "I feel I have characteristics in common with

Hope," he has said. "We're both cowards, womanizers, egotistical, vain. He was not a clown in the sense of Chaplin or Keaton. He was the guy next door, the man from the electric company. You really believed him." In 1979 Allen prepared a selection from Hope's films titled "My Favorite Comedian" for a public tribute. He said at that time that Hope's influence "appears throughout my work."

At thirteen, Woody became obsessed with magic (like Paul in his play *The Floating Lightbulb*) and would spend three or four hours a day teaching himself card tricks.

At fifteen, he fell in love with jazz and bought a soprano saxophone, which he taught himself to play. Later he switched to the clarinet. He still practices along with records at least an hour a day and plays once a week with a band at Michael's Pub in New York City.

Allen said of himself as a child, "Although I never laughed out loud then, I was a funny kid. My viewpoint was funny, and I said funny things." At the suggestion of a relative, he wrote some of those funny things down and sent them in to newspaper columnists under an assumed name. One that appeared in an Earl Wilson column was: "Woody Allen boasts that he just made a fortune downtown—he auctioned off his parking space."

The publication of these jokes led to a part-time job after school at a public relations firm. For two years he produced fifty gags a day to be used by the firm's clients. He was paid $25 a week. "I was utterly thrilled by the job," he said. "I thought I was in the heart of show business."

He was less thrilled about school. Although his compositions were always the ones read aloud in class, he graduated from high school with a 71 average. To satisfy his parents, Allen enrolled in college—twice. Both times he flunked out in his freshman year and went to work instead writing for comedians. At nineteen, he became a full-time NBC staff writer. He also got married that year to a girl he had known since high school. The marriage didn't work—they were both too young, he said—and they got divorced five years later.

Meanwhile Allen started seeing a psychoanalyst: "I was very unhappy. No particular reason, just a feeling I couldn't shake." He still goes to an analyst, sometimes as often as five times a week. Friends have described him as suffering from feelings of guilt, anger, and shame. He is also very self-critical. "I'm surprised at the amount of people that go to see my films," he has said. "All of my films have been personal failures," falling far short of "the grandiose plan I had in mind."

But Allen's personal problems have not stood in the way of his professional success. "I never get so depressed that it interferes with my work. I can go into a room every morning and churn it out."

By 1962 Woody Allen was one of the highest-paid writers in television comedy. Then his manager persuaded him to perform his lines on stage himself. "That took more courage than I knew I had," he said. "When I . . . decided to be a writer . . . it was in part because I was terrified of dealing with people, and I wanted to remain isolated. So it was an enormous wrench for me to go from the most ideally isolated situation to the most public situation available." He still prefers writing to either performing or directing.

According to his manager, Allen was "awful" at first: "Of course, he had good lines. But he was so scared and embarrassed and—rabbity. If you gave him an excuse not to go on, he'd take it." Two years later, however, Allen was earning $5,000 a week in well-known nightclubs, had made a record, and was a popular guest star on television comedy shows.

Although it hadn't taken him long to gain confidence on the stage, Allen still filled his act with stammers and hesitations—all carefully timed. Talking mainly about himself, he conveyed a sense of exclusion and inadequacy, of the little man against the elements. Of his wife he would frequently say, "We'd always have these deep philosophical discussions, and she always proved I didn't exist." He was so poor, he said, that he had a pet ant named Spot.

He had a phenomenal rapport with audiences. The critic Richard Schickel wrote, "All of us watching him, whatever our sizes or shapes, harbored a Woody Allen inside ourselves." Many viewers of his films, in which he usually stars, have the same feeling. But it would be wrong to assume that Woody Allen's real personality is the same as his stage personality. Although his clothes are the same onstage and off—beat-up sports jacket, open plaid sports shirts, loose pants—the effect is quite different.

Woody Allen is never "on" when he is not acting. He is an extremely hardworking, very private, shy man. His schedule, when he is not directing a film, is to get up at seven o'clock, write all day, and then go out for a late dinner with a few close friends. He doesn't drink, smoke, or take drugs. On meeting him for the first time, the film critic Janet Maslin wrote, "I was surprised to find him so solemn, so adult, so composed, so controlled, so unneurotic." And he has said of himself, "I'm preoccupied with problems and work, and I'm certainly not the delight of any party."

Interviewers are also surprised at the elegance of his home. He lives in a magnificent duplex penthouse apartment furnished in the style of a French country house. It overlooks New York's Central Park, and some of the opening scenes of his film *Manhattan* were shot from his terrace.

While Allen was winning acclaim as a stand-up comic, he also started contributing humorous essays to the *New Yorker* and other magazines. He still writes these pieces, which have been published in several collections. They are satires on language and culture, dealing with subjects as different as organized crime and philosophers and with titles like "If the Impressionists Had Been Dentists." Although he has claimed that he just tosses these off, his editor at the *New Yorker* described him as "a marvel of a willing and hardworking writer."

Woody Allen's goal at the beginning of his career, however,

was to be a playwright, and before he ever directed a film he had had two Broadway successes: *Don't Drink the Water* (1966) and *Play It Again, Sam* (1969).

Don't Drink the Water is about a Newark caterer who, while touring with his wife and daughter in an Eastern European country, gets into trouble for photographing a secret military installation. The play includes an Allen-like character who wins the girl after various bungling attempts to help. The play got mixed reviews: some critics complained that it was just a collection of one-liners. Allen claimed that he never intended it to be a classical play, but rather "the kind of very broad thing the Marx Brothers did. What fascinated me was the old formless farce." In any case, audiences liked it, and it played on Broadway for eighteen months.

Allen described his second Broadway comedy, *Play It Again, Sam*, as "an autobiographical story about a highly neurotic lover—an accumulation of themes that interest me: sex, adultery, extreme neuroses in romance, insecurity." Allan Felix (originally played by Allen himself) is a film critic whose wife has left him in bad shape: he can't even cook TV dinners; he sucks them frozen. (The play coincided with the breakup after three years of Allen's second marriage to Louise Lasser, who later won fame as Mary Hartman on television.)

Felix tries to model himself on Humphrey Bogart in order to make a new conquest. After several catastrophes, he falls in love with his best friend's wife (played by Diane Keaton, with whom Allen was having a romance in real life). Again, the play was not a critical success. "It is stringed with jokes, some hilarious, but it is not a play," wrote drama critic Walter Kerr. And again, audiences loved it, and it ran for more than a year.

Play It Again, Sam was made into a film in 1972. Although Allen wrote the screenplay and peformed in it, he chose an old pro, Herbert Ross, to direct. "I would never want to direct a play into a movie," he said. "I would only be interested in working on original projects for the screen."

No other Woody Allen plays were produced until *The Floating Lightbulb*, in 1981. It is the story of a poor Jewish family in Brooklyn in 1945, and a terribly shy boy who dreams of being a magician. Allen described it as a "modest little play," and critics, used to his adventurous filmmaking by this time, were disappointed that, as Frank Rich put it in the *New York Times*, "as a serious playwright, Mr. Allen is still learning his craft and finding his voice."

Woody Allen made his film debut not in his own movie but in *What's New, Pussycat?* (1965), a slapstick bedroom farce. He wrote the screenplay as "a Marx Brothers kind of script" and played the role of an undresser in a strip club. The stars, Peter Sellers and Peter O'Toole, changed the script, and Allen said of the film, "I never considered that one mine. I hated it, I hated making it, and it was the reason I became a director." Although *Pussycat* was panned by the critics, it was a box office hit, and it brought Woody Allen national fame.

His next project was *What's Up, Tiger Lily?* (1966). He and a group of friends improvised a comic English sound track for a cheaply made Japanese spy thriller. Phil Moscowitz (a Japanese actor with Allen's voice) and his allies and enemies are on a violent quest, for "it is written that he who has the best recipe for egg salad shall rule over heaven and earth." Most critics found the dialogue funny but thought that the joke didn't deserve a whole film. Allen himself hated the film and sued to stop its release. Other actors added jokes he said were "stupid," and his voice was dubbed in places.

Allen then performed in a second film for the producer of *Pussycat*. This one was *Casino Royale* (1967), a James Bond spoof. Allen was cast against type as Jimmy, Bond's nephew, a tough superspy. Most of his scenes were monologues, and he ad-libbed more than half his lines. "I never bothered to see *Casino Royale*," he said. "I knew it would be a horrible film. The set was a chaotic madhouse. I knew then that the only way to make a film is to control it completely."

Allen worked only once more as a hired hand, starring in a serious film, *The Front* (1976). He played a wisecracking, slightly neurotic loser who becomes involved in investigations during the McCarthy era because he acted as a front for blacklisted TV writers. "I didn't look at *The Front* as my chance to play Hamlet," Allen said at the time. "The reason I did *The Front* was that the subject was worthwhile."

Woody Allen's career as a filmmaker began in earnest in 1969 with *Take the Money and Run*. Since then he has had complete control of his films from conception through opening. He oversees the credits, the ads, and the theaters where the movies play, as well as making every artistic decision.

In all his films, Allen has tended to cast people he knows and trusts (former wives, friends, and lovers like Louise Lasser, Tony Roberts, and Diane Keaton). He has said that he does this because he is shy. His collaborations on scripts, also with friends, have involved what Marshall Brickman (coauthor of two films) described as "highly stylized conversations"—talking and talking and talking and then remembering what was good and putting it down on paper.

Allen allows his actors to improvise and shoots much more footage than he can use. His direction, he has said, "consists usually of 'faster,' 'louder,' and 'more real.'" But the atmosphere on his sets is not relaxed. Gene Wilder, who played a successful doctor who leaves his wife for a sheep named Daisy in a segment of *Everything You Always Wanted to Know about Sex*, described the set of that movie as "people talking in whispers, serious looks on Woody's face. He communicates through silence."

Woody Allen's first five films—from *Take the Money and Run* through *Love and Death*—are what he has called "comedy that was strictly for laughs." Although they become progressively more skillful, they have a certain style in common. Their composition is purely functional, the gags are more important than the narrative, the camera is tied down, and the movie is made with cuts.

In 1974, he said, "The closest analogy to my films would be the Tom and Jerry cartoons. A guy runs out and you smash him on the head with something and he doesn't die and he doesn't bleed and it's past and you clear the decks for the next joke right away." These films all received good reviews and were reasonably successful at the box office, although his urban humor was most popular in big cities.

The first film, *Take the Money and Run*, Allen has said, was "strictly a learning experience." It is a mock documentary, which he wrote with his high-school friend Mickey Rose. In a series of short, funny sketches he documents the inept criminal history of Virgil Starkwell (Allen), "known to police in six states for assault, armed robbery, and possession of a wart," as the earnest narrator relates. In one sketch the gun he carves out of soap and blackens with shoe polish for his prison break dissolves in the rain.

In *Bananas* (also written with Mickey Rose), he is more experimental. He parodies several scenes from famous films and also moves his characters out of New York. Allen plays Fielding Melish, an apolitical products tester whose products tend to attack him. He somehow becomes the leader of a revolution in South America in the course of trying to impress Nancy, a fashionably liberal girl (played by Louise Lasser). *Bananas* begins and ends with an appearance by Howard Cosell, being himself. At first he is commenting in the midst of a political coup; then he is ringside on the eve of Fielding's marriage to Nancy. In this film, too, Allen has said, his method was "to have a thin story line to hang the comedy sequences on."

Everything You Always Wanted to Know about Sex is "the first picture where I've cared about anything but the jokes. I wanted to do something where the color was really pretty and controlled, and the moves contributed and everything worked." In each of the seven episodes, based on questions in the popular sex manual, Allen parodies a type of film or television program and experiments with color and sets. Although critics found some episodes tasteless or tedious, almost all agreed that "What Happens during Ejaculation?" is brilliant. The scene takes place inside the male body, at a NASA-like headquarters, where Allen plays a cowardly sperm.

The idea for *Sleeper* came from this successful episode. *Sleeper* is a science fiction satire about the operator of a health food store who goes into the hospital for an ulcer operation in the 1970s and wakes up after two hundred years of frozen animation. The world he finds is ruled by a voice coming from the television set. All needs are filled by robots and machines, like the silver ball that can be rubbed for instant pleasure ("even worse than California," he says). Allen wrote the script with Marshall Brickman, who had written jokes for his nightclub act in the sixties.

With this film Allen makes a slight shift in style. He uses more physical comedy and pantomime, and the humor is based more on a concept than on basically unconnected gags. He uses the framework of the future to comment on sophisticated modern life. In *Sleeper*, also, he has said, "I became aware of visuals. Since then, I've gotten deeper and deeper into visually arresting films."

Love and Death is another good-looking film, shot in "soft, autumnal colors." This time he uses the past (nineteenth-century Russia) as his framework. Boris Grushenko (Allen), a "militant coward," tells the story of his life, including his fateful wavering over the decision to kill Napoleon: "If I don't kill him he'll make war all through Europe. But murder . . . What would Socrates say?" He later ponders his death before a firing squad: "There are worse things in life than death," he says the night before. The film also tells of Boris's passion for his pseudointellectual cousin Sonia (Diane Keaton), who gets him into this mess.

Allen has said that *Love and Death* makes a "slight satirical point about dying, and war, and the transitory quality of love." He has also said that "the serious intent underlying the humor was not very apparent to most audiences. Laughter submerges

Woody Allen and Diane Keaton in a scene from *Annie Hall*. PHOTO: United Press International

everything else. That's why I felt that, with *Annie Hall*, I would have to reduce some of the laughter. I didn't want to destroy the credibility for the sake of the laugh."

Annie Hall, his next film, led the way to a series of films that are more human and less like cartoons. It is the story of a love affair, told through the drifting recollections of Alvy Singer (Allen), a melancholy, self-critical comedy writer. It is a film about relationships, not a farce. In the opening monologue Alvy says, "Annie and I broke up." And he asks, "Where did the screw-up come?" *Annie Hall* has some funny anecdotes and one-liners, but there are fewer of them and they are tied more closely to the characters. For example, the hilarious scene where Alvy and Annie chase their live lobster dinner around the kitchen (he suggests luring it from behind the refrigerator with butter sauce) occurs while they are getting to know each other.

The Allen character in this film is more complex than ever before and has real feelings. When he goes to California to try to get back the now sun-tanned, self-assured Annie, he feels sad and insecure.

Of the change from the earlier films to *Annie Hall*, Allen said at the time: "In order to grow, I knew I'd have to deepen the work—to use comedy in the service of ideas, or more genuine satire, or emotional exploration. It's an attempt to develop."

In this film he also develops his style as a filmmaker. The camera is allowed to move, and there is a deliberate three-color scheme: the romantic New York scenes were shot on overcast days or at sundown; scenes from the past have a nostalgic, golden-yellow hue; and the California scenes were shot right into the sun so that people almost seem to evaporate. He uses a split screen, animation, instant replay, and even subtitles in a scene where Alvy is looking at Annie's photographs:

ALVY: They're wonderful, you know. They have a quality.

(SUBTITLE: You are a great-looking girl.)
ANNIE: Well, I would like to take a serious photography
            course.
(SUBTITLE: He probably thinks I'm a yo-yo.)

Although Allen claims that *Annie Hall* is a work of fiction, the main character, like Allen, is a writer and also, like Allen, has a relationship with Diane Keaton (whose real last name is Hall). The film also reflects Allen's feeling of being a Jew in a Protestant world. (On first meeting Alvy, Annie exclaims, "You're what Grammy Hall would call a real Jew!") And it is flavored with some of his favorite prejudices, including his dislike of California. "I can't live in any city where the only cultural advantage is that you can make a right turn on a red light," says Alvy.

Annie Hall was a hit. It won four Oscars—for screenplay (written with Marshall Brickman), direction, best picture, and best actress (Diane Keaton). It won the New York and National Film Critics awards, a Directors Guild award, and raves from the major American critics. But Allen remained unsatisfied: "*Annie Hall*, to me, was a very middle-class picture, and that's why I think people liked it. It was the reinforcement of middle-class values."

Allen decided to make his next film a "serious" one. As early as 1968 he had been naming Ingmar Bergman as the filmmaker who most influenced him: "Bergman interests me more than anyone because of the consummate marriage of technique, theatricality, and themes that are both personally important to me and that have gigantic size—death, the meaning of life, the question of religious faith." He said of his serious film while he was making it—as if anticipating the criticism—"I'm feeling my way, just as when I was beginning as a cabaret comedian. I have to watch out for touches of other people in my work."

Interiors, the only one of his films in which Woody Allen does not appear, is a psychological drama about a genteel New England family—a controlling mother, a distant father, and three unhappy daughters. One of them, Renata, a talented and successful poet played by Diane Keaton, Allen said, "articulates all my personal concerns. . . . You have a sense of immortality that your work will live on after you, which is nonsense. . . . Renata comes to realize in the movie . . . that the only thing anyone has any chance with is human relationships."

Like *Annie Hall*, this film is about how and why relationships fail, but it has a much graver tone. Allen's directorial style changed, too. "I was always telling them to play smaller, don't do so much . . . whereas in a comedy film, it's always louder and faster."

Interiors split the critics into two camps: many found it a pretentious attempt to copy Bergman; others admired it. Allen was nominated for an Academy Award as best director.

With his next film, Woody Allen bounced back firmly into the critics' good graces, winning the New York Film Critics Circle award for best director. *Manhattan* (again written with Marshall Brickman) returned to the romantic comedy style of *Annie Hall*. Allen said about the film, "I wanted to make an amusing film, but a film with feelings that went deeper than *Annie Hall*."

Manhattan is a straight narrative about Isaac Davis (Allen), a successful TV writer who leaves his job to write a serious novel. The film portrays his relationships with seventeen-year-old Tracy ("I'm going out with a girl who does homework," he mocks himself) and Mary (Diane Keaton), a neurotic writer and the mistress of his married best friend Yale (Tony Roberts). It deals, in his words, with the problem of trying "to live a decent life amid all the junk of contemporary culture—the temptations, the seductions."

Allen intended *Manhattan* to be "a metaphor for everything wrong with our culture." And there is much that is wrong with the slick, upper-class New York people of this film, where Mary makes pretentious comments about art, Yale broods deeply over buying a Porsche, and Isaac tries to run over his former wife's female lover.

The film is visually sophisticated. Shot in black and white, it uses compositions with depth and shadow. Richard Schickel, in *Time* magazine, called it "the perfect blending of style and substance, humor and humanity."

Stardust Memories, Allen's next film, though also a comic drama, stirred some of the same controversy as *Interiors*. It is the story of Sandy Bates (Allen), a filmmaker attending a weekend film seminar on his own films at the Hotel Stardust. He doesn't want to make comedies anymore but his vulgar, fawning fans criticize him for his recent seriousness. This time Allen was accused of copying Fellini, whose 8½ is about a director at an artistic and spiritual impasse. *Stardust Memories* is filled with ideas about comedy, suffering celebrity, and the search for the right woman.

Although Woody Allen insisted that it was wrong to identify Sandy Bates with himself, many critics and audiences felt his hostility directed at them in the film.

A Midsummer Night's Sex Comedy, released two years later, has none of the bitterness of *Stardust Memories*, but it lacks the comic spirit of his other films. It is about the romantic intermingling of three couples in a country house at the turn of the century. Among them are a Wall Street broker and crackpot inventor (Allen), a lady-killing doctor (Tony Roberts), and a worldly femme fatale (Mia Farrow, Allen's current girl friend in real life). Critics described the film as "amiable" and "pretty" and "entertaining," but almost always as "slight."

They used only superlatives for his next film, however, several critics hailing *Zelig* as Allen's best and wittiest. *Zelig* is a mock-documentary like *Take the Money and Run*, but much smoother

and surer. It recounts the life of Leonard Zelig (Allen), supposedly a national figure of the 1920s and 30s. Newspapers dub
him "the chameleon man" because he takes on the physical and
mental characteristics of those around him, from black jazz
musicians to bearded rabbis. Mia Farrow plays Dr. Eudora
Fletcher, a psychiatrist who solemnly dedicates herself to curing
Zelig and ends up falling in love with him.

The story is told through old newsreels blended perfectly with
new material. Allen fits convincingly among the entourages of
both Pope Pius XI and Adolf Hitler. There is commentary on his
historical significance by modern intellectuals like Susan Sontag
and footage of his sessions with Dr. Fletcher during which he
becomes a psychiatrist himself. He is treating two pairs of
Siamese twins with split personalities, he tells her. "I receive fees
from eight people."

Allen has finished another film, *Broadway Danny Rose*,
which will be released in early 1984. It was kept under tight cover
before and during production, as are all his films, and there is no
way to guess what it will be like. Allen has said, "There is a
tendency among comedians to hit on something the public likes
and then just grind it out for the rest of their lives. . . . I want to
write all sorts of things. . . ."

Robert Altman with Lauren Bacall during the filming of *Health*. PHOTO:
United Press International

Robert Altman

ROBERT ALTMAN has had only two real commercial successes—M*A*S*H and Nashville—and his films are almost always controversial. They are called poetical and pretentious, masterpieces and mishmashes. Altman himself is also controversial. A large, commanding man, he has infuriated and bewildered studio heads by insisting on doing things his own way. Yet most critics and serious filmgoers regard Robert Altman as an important filmmaker. He has directed films with a personal style, and he has directed many of them—fifteen since M*A*S*H, his antiwar black comedy (not to be confused with the television series), which made him the hottest director of 1970.

19

When he became Hollywood's whiz kid, Robert Altman was no kid at all. He was forty-five years old. "I think that if I'd done *M*A*S*H* when I was thirty-two," he said, "I'd be a hack today. I think if I'd gotten that much adulation I would have become very cocky." Instead he spent those thirteen years on the outskirts of the film industry, directing industrial films for corporations and episodes for television series.

Robert Altman was born on February 20, 1925, in Kansas City, Missouri, the oldest of three children. His father was a very successful insurance salesman and a habitual gambler. Altman also is a gambler and even made a film on the subject, *California Split* ("a celebration of gambling," he called it). To him, gambling is not a sin or a disease; it provides "the excitement of being near danger."

Altman describes his upbringing as "normal" and "uneventful," and his family as "very American, commercially oriented" people. For the conservative old-money family of his film *A Wedding*, he drew on his own. "All my aunts sang, or played the harp, and they'd all gone to Europe, and spoke French." He named the movie family's matriarch "Nettie" after his grandmother.

Not a good student, though talented in math and drawing, Altman majored in mathematical engineering at the University of Missouri. But he dropped out and joined the army at eighteen, when he also abandoned the Catholicism he had grown up with.

As a child, Altman has said, "I just loved the movies. I saw them all, went all the time." Once he played hooky from school in order to see *Viva Villa!* with Wallace Beery. He entered the theater at noon and didn't emerge until nine o'clock that night, when his parents dragged him out. Another time, when he had the mumps, he climbed out his window to see *King Kong*.

Altman has said that the most important influences on him were the directors of the films he saw in his childhood— especially Howard Hawks and John Huston. He also remembers discovering the English films of the forties; Fellini's *La Dolce Vita*; and Bergman's films, especially *Persona*. "But the best film I've seen *ever*," he said in 1974, "is *Last Tango in Paris*. That film advanced me twenty years. . . . Because of it I was able to shoot a nude scene in *Thieves Like Us* that I would have been embarrassed to do before and would have covered up."

In the army during World War II, Altman flew numerous B-24 bombing missions over Borneo and the Dutch East Indies. In general, though, he tried to get by "as comfortably as possible." He has said, "I organized an officers' club so I could get to the liquor easiest. My attitude was pretty much like that of Elliott Gould and Donald Sutherland in *M*A*S*H*."

Having written letters and short stories during the war, Altman came home with the idea of becoming a writer. He tried to sell magazine stories, radio shows, and film scripts with little success. He then spent a year in New York City writing, though he actually earned his living by tattooing license numbers on dogs.

When Altman returned to Kansas City, he got a job with the Calvin Company, which made documentary training and sales films for corporations like Gulf Oil and Caterpillar Tractors. There he spent the next eight years becoming a professional filmmaker. "It was a great training period. I wrote, directed, produced, and edited. There wasn't anything I wasn't into." He also had the freedom to do the technical experiments that have always interested him. For one film, for instance, he recorded all the dialogue in a car.

Twice during the 1950s Altman left Kansas City and tried to make it in Hollywood. Both times he had to retreat home "stone broke." Then in 1955 a man he knew asked him to make a film about juvenile delinquents. He wrote, produced, and directed a feature called *The Delinquents*, which was sold to United Artists and got mediocre reviews. Altman himself now owns most of the prints and won't show the film to anyone.

Having left his job for good, Altman, with a partner, made a documentary called *The James Dean Story* for Warner Brothers. It was based on photographs, film clips, reenactments, and interviews with the star's relatives and friends. "I started with the idea of taking Dean to bits," Altman said, "but in the end I guess we all got caught up in the mystique of the man." Altman's later attempts to debunk myths would be more successful.

The film did not do well, but Alfred Hitchcock noticed it and hired Altman to direct some of his half-hour TV mystery shows. Altman directed two, but complained to the producer that the third was "awful." As it turned out, this was a script she personally had developed. "Which left me one way to go," Altman said. "Out."

On the basis of the two Hitchcock credits, and in spite of a reputation for being difficult, Altman was able to build a successful career as a television director. He was the writer, director, and/or producer of more than three hundred hours of television programs. Although he didn't like or respect the work, he says that television taught him useful skills, such as how to shoot fast and cheap. Many of his films have cost less than $2 million, which is very low for Hollywood.

Within limits, Altman filmed TV shows in his own unorthodox style, often losing his job for doing so. One series he worked on was called "Combat." Because the star could never die, Altman would establish another actor as an important character, use him three or four times, and then kill him off. He was finally fired for an antiwar episode he shot without a script. "Kids watch this show," he was told, "and there's not enough jokes for them."

In 1963, at a time when he was making $125,000 a year and had his pick of anything on television, Robert Altman quit. "I finally got tired of the compromise involved in television. . . . By the nature of the medium, it can't be art. What you're doing, you're not doing directly to the audience. There is an intermediary in there, whether it's the agency, or the network, or the sponsors."

During the next few years he got deeper and deeper into debt. He had always spent more than he earned, and there was also the gambling. Then in 1966 he was hired by Warner Brothers to direct *Countdown*, a film about a flight to the moon. Shooting was almost over when Jack Warner saw part of the film in which Altman had two actors talking at the same time. He fired Altman in a fury, cut the film, and added some scenes at the end. The result, according to the *New York Times* critic who saw it, "makes the moon seem just as dull as Mother Earth."

Altman struggled for two more years before he got to direct his first major film, *That Cold Day in the Park*. He wrote the script himself, based on a book to which he and a partner had bought the rights. The story of a psychotic thirty-two-year-old virgin who traps a twenty-year-old boy in her apartment, it was a critical and financial disaster. In fact, Ingo Preminger, producer of *M*A*S*H*, claims that if he had seen that film, he would never have hired Altman. As it was, Altman was his fifteenth choice.

M*A*S*H is the story of two irreverent doctors in a Mobile Army Surgical Hospital in Korea. Hawkeye (Donald Sutherland) and Trapper John (Elliott Gould) are serious surgeons—the best—but less than serious military men. When they are called to Japan to operate on a congressman's son, they bring along their golf clubs. Major Margaret Houlihan, whose role Altman expanded from a cameo of nine lines to that of a major character, calls the army her "home" and is the exact opposite. She is the butt of *M*A*S*H*'s ultimate practical joke. She earns the nickname Hot Lips when her passionate lovemaking with a Bible-toting officer is broadcast over the camp's public address system. Behind the antiwar and counterculture humor, however, is the ever-present gore of the battlefield operating room.

The film was a shocking success. Altman attributes it to timing. Protest against the war in Vietnam was at a high. *M*A*S*H* was chosen as the best film at the Cannes Film Festival and grossed about $40 million, and Altman was nominated for an Academy Award.

Altman earned only a flat fee of $75,000, but *M*A*S*H* got him out of debt and, more important, gave him the means to ensure his independence. In 1963 Altman had founded his own production company and had begun to develop movie projects. After *M*A*S*H*, this production company became Lion's Gate Films, which over the next ten years grew into a ministudio. There, Altman could handle everything from script conferences to film editing. He needed the studios only for financing and distribution. Lion's Gate stayed afloat until 1981, but it was not a profit-making venture. Altman kept plowing the money he earned from his films back into the company.

At the peak of his commercial success, Robert Altman, typically, refused to give Hollywood what it wanted—another *M*A*S*H*. "I always try to push each film a little farther," he explained, "to do things that are a little more difficult for me, to see how far I can make them work."

After making a war film that deglamourized war, Altman played with other traditional movie genres in many of his later films: the caper (*Brewster McCloud*), the psychological thriller (*Images*), the Western (*McCabe and Mrs. Miller* and *Buffalo Bill and the Indians*), the buddy picture (*California Split*), the detective film (*The Long Goodbye*), the period gangster film (*Thieves Like Us*), the musical (*Nashville*), the romantic comedy (*A Wedding* and *A Perfect Couple*), and the science fiction film (*Quintet*). The reason he gave for doing this: "It's telling the audience the medium you are using and, at the same time, reminding them that it *is* only a film."

The films themselves explore themes that interest Altman: what he has called "the flexible boundary between sanity and insanity," and American life today, often as seen through its myths and rituals. Most of the films deal with outsiders, he has said, "people who don't belong there and are trying to cope. I like to tell stories about an alien wandering into a strange place."

Of his next fifteen films, only *Nashville* earned him the great commercial success and critical acclaim that *M*A*S*H* seemed to assure him. *Nashville* followed twenty-four characters through five days on the country music scene. It also drew the comparison between politicians and musical performers. A thin thread of plot holds these elements together. The campaign manager for a third-party candidate is trying to recruit performers for a huge rally. He is ambitious and hypocritical, but so are they.

Altman's characters, who often are not on the screen for long, all suggest great depth. Sometimes it is done with a small detail, like the unmatching wig of Haven Hamilton, the country and western king, or the offhand remark made by the rock couple that they are registered Democrats because her father is.

Altman encouraged his actors to create biographies for their characters and to research their parts. Gwen Welles, who played Sueleen Gay, a waitress and pathetically untalented singer, worked for a while in an airport restaurant before acting in the movie. He is also very perceptive in casting. Keith Carradine, who played Tom, the cool, promiscuous rock singer, said, "Once he hires you for a part, that's it. It means you're right for it and you can't do anything wrong." The casting choice in *Nashville* for which Altman has received most admiration is his decision to give Lily Tomlin the role of Linnea Reese, the gospel singer and mother of two deaf children with whom she communicates in sign language.

Although there were some dissenters, *Nashville* won awards for best director, best film, and best supporting actress (Lily Tomlin) from the New York Film Critics Circle and received five Oscar nominations.

Most of Altman's other films broke even at the box office, but not much more, and met with mixed reviews. Some, like *The*

Long Goodbye (based on a Raymond Chandler story), were marketed wrong by studio executives who missed their satirical intent. But others, like *McCabe and Mrs. Miller*, are also inherently controversial.

McCabe is the story of a man who builds up a frontier town with the help of a tough madam (Mrs. Miller, played by Julie Christie), then is killed by big businessmen who want to take it over. McCabe looks like a Western hero. Altman cast Warren Beatty for the part to ensure that. He is actually something of a fool. ("If you want to make out you're such a fancy dude," Mrs. Miller chides, "you might wear something besides that cheap jockey club cologne.")

The film evoked very different responses from two prominent critics. Pauline Kael, writing in the *New Yorker*, called it "a beautiful pipedream of a movie—a fleeting, almost diaphanous vision of what frontier life might have been." John Simon, on the other hand, in the *New York Times*, complained that the film was "pretentious," "full of plot elements that are left dangling," and "crawling with audiovisual mannerisms."

The two critics responded in opposite ways to Robert Altman's style and to the result he aims for: a film that "will have the effect of making an audience leave the theater impressed and overwhelmed and yet unable to articulate what it has seen, because the picture will have worked on so many senses at the same time." That style is reflected in how his pictures look, how they sound, how they tell their tales, and how they are made.

Robert Altman's films are filled with visual details. He has used the wider screen provided by Panavision for almost all of his pictures. Even so, they often seem to overflow with people and action.

Altman also uses color in a very deliberate way. He wanted *McCabe and Mrs. Miller*, which takes place in 1902, to have the faded look of an old photograph. He also wanted to suggest the lighting of the time—gas or oil lanterns. He and his cinematographer spent hours and hours testing on location before shooting. They finally decided to manipulate the film negative by techniques called flashing and fogging. *Buffalo Bill and the Indians*, Altman's film about the selling of history ("Truth is whatever gets the loudest applause," Bill says), was also supposed to have an antique look. For this film, Altman removed all the blue in the lab, so that yellows, heavy reds, and blacks were exaggerated.

He wanted the film *Three Women*, based on his dream about two young girls who meet in a California desert community and switch personalities, to have a dreamlike quality. For the scenes in the desert, the negatives were overexposed and printed up to give them a faded look. The interiors were done the opposite way. He picked locales very carefully for colors, and the wardrobes and decorations of the apartments tended toward yellows, pinks, and purples—the colors of the desert.

In *Popeye*, his live-action musical version of the comic strip, he wanted a sense of reality at the beginning, even though the characters are two-dimensional. "We didn't go for diffusion," he said, "or anything to give it a sense of distance or antiquity. . . . I muted the colors, the town. As the film progresses, the colors become more specific, cartoony. The reds come out. The wardrobe changes."

The sound of an Altman film is also distinctive. To those who criticize his overlapping dialogue as "inaudible," he answers that it is intended to "give the audience the sense of the dialogue, the emotional feeling rather than the literal word; that's the way sound is in real life." In order to do this well, he developed a special eight-track sound system called Lion's Gate Sound. It records the voices of the actors on separate tracks which can be balanced later. In *Nashville*, he added sixteen tracks for the music.

Altman also often uses a repeated aural theme in his films, usually to add a note of irony or self-consciousness. The muddled loudspeaker announcements in *M*A*S*H*, the Leonard Cohen ballads in *McCabe and Mrs. Miller*, the blaring political slogans from the van in *Nashville*, are some of them. He leaves room for these during shooting and then plugs them in during the editing or sound-mixing stage. Many of these ideas were not even conceived until after the shooting was over.

Perhaps the most controversial element of Altman's style is his focus on behavior and character rather than plot. This is partly a reaction to his many years in television, where he was dealing with hundreds and hundreds of stories in which everything had to be spelled out. "In most films," he once said, "so much specific information is provided that the audience is allowed to be totally uninvolved. I try to make an audience do as much work as they would do reading a novel."

The loose structure of Altman's films suits well his collaborative style of filmmaking. Over the years he has assembled a team of actors and technical people who work on many of his films. Tommy Thompson, for instance, who was assistant director and associate producer on many of Altman's films, began working with him during his TV days. The actors in his "repertory company" include Michael Murphy, Shelley Duvall, Keith Carradine, and Geraldine Chaplin. The idea, he has said, "is to have people around that you know are really cooperative: you want to know that they are in tune with what you are doing and that they respect what you are doing." This also contributes to the success of his casting. "I use a lot of repeats because when I work with an actor I learn what their range is."

Altman is also known for giving people a chance and encouraging creativity. Shelley Duvall had never acted before she met Altman at a party. He gave her a role in *Brewster McCloud*, the story of a boy who wants to fly and a satire on various American follies. Since then she has appeared in many of his films, perhaps most notably as Olive Oyl in *Popeye*.

Joan Tewkesbury, who had directed and adapted only plays,

walked in off the street as an admirer. Altman immediately made her script girl on *McCabe and Mrs. Miller* and then gave her two scripts to write—*Thieves Like Us* and *Nashville*. *Thieves Like Us* was based on a book, but for *Nashville*, she said, he told her only to have someone die at the end. "Otherwise my only instructions were to go to Nashville and see what I could find out." Altman himself added the political theme when the script was finished.

Altman gives his actors an extraordinary amount of freedom and encouragement to improvise: "I don't look for someone to fill a specific part or role so much as I look for an actor who can tell me what that role is about." Some of this is done in front of the camera, but much is done in rehearsal and rewriting. As an extreme example, Shelley Duvall wrote 80 percent of her dialogue in *Three Women*.

In *Nashville* the actors who played country and western singers were encouraged to write their own songs with the help of a professional. Ronee Blakeley, who played the reigning queen of country music in the film, also wrote the scene in which she broke down before an audience. Altman substituted this rambling monologue about her childhood for the scene he had planned. He has said of actors, "The less I impose myself on them, the better the work gets, constantly."

With the actor John Considine, Altman wrote the script for his film *A Wedding*, a satire that observes forty-two characters on a wedding day. Altman and Considine blocked out the scenes according to a wedding schedule and made an outline of character sketches, but wrote no dialogue. "All the actors took these parts without really knowing much of anything about their characters," Altman said. "The minute we had the picture cast I put [two writers] on the film. . . . All of the actors were free to go to any of us to work on their characters' background stories— . . . I had the actors write out their characters' histories—and by the time we began shooting, each actor had a lot of information to work with. And we did encourage the actors to use as much of themselves and their personalities as they would allow themselves to do."

Keith Carradine—who, besides Tom in *Nashville*, played an innocent cowboy in *McCabe and Mrs. Miller*, and the boyish bank robber in *Thieves Like Us*—describes Altman from the actor's point of view: "He sees things in actors they may not even seen in themselves." Paul Newman, who played Buffalo Bill in *Buffalo Bill and the Indians* and Essex in *Quintet*, said that "the most marvelous thing is that there are no egos on the set. . . . No one has any pride of ownership."

As a result, Altman's actors are usually devoted to him. The whole cast of *Nashville*, for instance, worked at rock-bottom wages just to be in his film.

Screenwriters (except for Joan Tewkesbury) are less fond of Altman, however. In fact, he has rarely used the same one twice. Besides allowing his actors to improvise, Altman does a great deal of rewriting himself, often the morning before shooting. Yet he shows no more reverence for his own scripts than for anyone else's. Susannah York, who starred in *Images*, the story of a schizophrenic woman who kills her husband, came up with a better ending than his. Altman immediately struck two sets that were already built in order to use it.

Altman has referred to the screenplay as "a selling tool" for getting financing and after that, "not much more than a production schedule." He said, "I don't consider the dialogue, in most cases, part of the writing. I consider that part of the acting. . . . To me, the writing—the authorship—is in the concept of the film."

Altman himself is responsible for developing the concept and for conveying it to the actors. He does this, in part, by talking to them about their roles, the other characters, and the whole film. He also sets up "the stimuli which the actors will respond to." For *McCabe and Mrs. Miller*, a real town was built on top of a mountain in Canada, building by building, as each new character entered. The actors picked out houses to live in and had square dances at night in the saloon. For *California Split*, Altman hired Amarillo Slim, the champion poker player, to play himself. His contribution to the film, the director said, "was not so much what the audience sees as it was an environment to the people who were there."

Altman always tries to shoot in sequence and to keep the cast together for the full shooting. The result is a close-knit group that meets after work to watch the film from each day's shooting. Carol Burnett said of her experience on the set of *A Wedding*, "It was like summer camp. We all had our kids with us and we had a hoot." A chef is often part of Altman's entourage, and the director admits drinking a Scotch—or two—after hours. ("I don't drink while I'm working," Altman has said. "But I work a lot while I'm drinking.") He is known, however, as a workaholic.

Family life would seem to be a likely victim of this robust man of large appetites, which include a fondness for women, but his wife Kathryn (his third), a witty and elegant woman, seems to be able to cope with him. They have been married for twenty-one years and have two sons. (He also has three children from his previous marriages.) Altman describes her as "terrific" and has said of their marriage, "We really live quite separate lives, but we live them together." And she has said, "He has driven me crazy but he has never bored me."

Lion's Gate, Altman's production company, began to produce other directors' films in the mid-1970s: Alan Rudolph's *Welcome to L.A.* and *Remember My Name*, Robert Benton's *The Late Show*, and Robert Young's *Rich Kids*. Altman saw this, in part, as a way to keep his technical staff employed, but he also wanted to give other filmmakers "the opportunity to make movies the way they want to make them."

In 1979 Lion's Gate greatly expanded and moved into a much larger complex. Unfortunately this move coincided with a downswing in Altman's career. *Quintet*, a film about people playing a morbid game in a bleak future world, which Altman made when his father was dying, was universally panned. *Health*, the story of forty-seven characters at a health food convention, was delayed two years and then released only timidly. Finally, *Popeye* was a critical disappointment and resulted in lawsuits over its great cost ($20 million).

In 1981 Robert Altman sold Lion's Gate. "Suddenly, no one answered my phone calls," he said. "I had no place to turn." He accepted this as the price for being innovative and looked forward to a period of renewal. "I'm merely taking a sabbatical," he said at the time, "and I'm doing something that I've always wanted to do. . . . I think I've been too isolated. I've denied myself the experience of paying attention to the whole spectrum of art: to working in the theater, in opera, in ballet."

Since then, he has directed two short plays by Frank South in New York, both of which got good reviews. He also did a well-publicized staging of Ed Graczyk's *Come Back to the 5 & Dime Jimmy Dean, Jimmy Dean* with Karen Black, Sandy Dennis, and Cher, which failed on Broadway.

But Altman seems to be easing himself back into film. He videotaped the South plays for cable TV. He also shot *Jimmy Dean* in 16-millimeter to be blown up to 35-millimeter for release to art theaters. The film got much better reviews than the play.

For the future, after directing an opera, he plans a film version of another play. "I left the major studios," he said recently. "I didn't leave the movies."

Mel Brooks as the star of *High Anxiety*. PHOTO: Courtesy of 20th Century-Fox

Mel Brooks

"As long as I am on the soapbox, farts will be heard," proclaimed Mel Brooks in a flash of the sort of humor that some find hilarious and others find vulgar. And Brooks has been on the soapbox a long time. "As early as I can remember," he said, "I was expected to perform."

Melvin Kaminsky was born on the kitchen table of a tenement in Williamsburg, a predominantly Jewish section of Brooklyn, on June 28, 1926. He never got to know his father, who died when he was two and a half. Some critics and friends see his intense need for approval and fear of death as stemming in part from this loss, which he still mourns. Gene Wilder once described his mental image of Brooks: "I see him standing bare-chested on the top of a mountain, shouting 'Look at me!' and 'Don't let me die!'"

Brooks grew up during the depression. For many years his mother worked long hours in the garment district and then brought more work home at night. But when Melvin was born, his three older brothers were all working so that she could stay home with her beautiful blue-eyed baby. Brooks remembers a delightfully happy childhood, reveling in the adoration of his family. "I was always being tossed in the air, kissed, adored, and pinched." His mother, he said, "had this exuberant joy of living, and she infected me with that. . . . She really was responsible for the growth of my imagination."

His peers were less adoring. They saw him as a little, funny-looking kid who didn't smoke. "But I could talk better than any of them," Brooks said. "I wormed my way in with jokes." If the ebullient side of his humor was born in the family circle, the more caustic side grew up in the outside world. "It comes from not being kissed by a girl until you're sixteen. It comes from feeling that, as a Jew and as a person, you don't fit into the mainstream of American society."

For two years when Melvin was in high school, the Kaminskys lived next door to Buddy Rich, the famous drummer, who gave Mel occasional lessons. When he was fourteen Mel began working during the summers in resort hotels in the Catskill Mountains, the training ground for many great Jewish comedians. He did menial work for room and board and eight dollars a week, and in his free time was allowed to play pool *tummler* (part social director, part buffoon). His main gag was to walk out on the diving board with a suitcase in each hand, announce, "Business is terrible; I can't go on," and jump in.

The summer he was sixteen he was hired as a drummer and part-time *tummler* at one of these hotels. It was then that he changed his name (Brooks is based on Brookman, his mother's maiden name). He didn't want to be confused with the jazz trumpeter Max Kaminsky. That summer two pivotal events occurred: the house comic got sick and Brooks finished the season for him, and he met a saxophone player from a nearby hotel named Sid Caesar.

But Brooks didn't get a chance to develop his taste for performing. World War II was going on, and a month after he graduated from high school, he enlisted in the army. His job was to deactivate land mines ahead of the infantry, but he remembers an unrelated highlight of his wartime service. After the Battle of the Bulge, the Germans made a propaganda pitch to the soldiers over a loudspeaker. Brooks answered with an imitation of Al Jolson singing "Toot Toot Tootsie."

For several months after the war he did shows for enlisted men and officers' clubs. Then he became director, actor, and stagehand in a third-rate summer stock company in New Jersey. When it folded for lack of funds, he went back to the Catskills as a house comic.

In 1947, his acquaintance Sid Caesar asked him to help prepare a revue for television. His first contribution was "Nonentities in the News." Their collaboration lasted almost ten years, through "Your Show of Shows" (with Imogene Coca and Carl Reiner), "Caesar's Hour," and a number of specials. Brooks started out at a weekly salary of $50 and peaked at $5,000.

Caesar's team of writers worked together in endless high-pitched jam sessions. Brooks would jump on furniture and bang his head against the wall. "I had an audience of experts and they showed me no mercy. . . . I was immensely ambitious. It was like I was screaming at the universe to pay attention. Like I had to make *God* laugh."

For Caesar, Brooks created the interview as a new form of comic art. His first invented character was a jungle boy who was brought to New York and put on display. The interviewer asked him, "What in this big city do you fear most, Jungle Boy?" "Buick," Caesar answered. "Buick stronger than lion. Must wait for eyes to go dark before attacking it. When Buick sleep, I sneak up and punch in grill. Buick die."

These years were disastrous for Brooks psychologically. He was depressed and had acute anxiety attacks. "There were fourteen or fifteen occasions when I seriously thought of killing myself," he said. Between 1951 and 1957 he saw a psychoanalyst two to four times a week.

In 1959 his seven-year marriage to a Broadway dancer broke up, separating him from the four children he adores. His problems, he has said, were connected "with accepting life as an adult in the real world. . . . It meant no longer being the baby, the adorable one. It meant being a father figure." He has stayed very close to his daughter and three sons, whom he describes as "these nice friends I've grown."

When "Caesar's Hour" went off the air in 1958, Brooks was again thrown off balance emotionally as well as financially. He tried a variety of projects: he worked on two short-lived Broadway musicals; he wrote a screenplay ("Marriage Is a Dirty Rotten Fraud"), which he couldn't sell; he contributed sketches to a number of TV variety shows; and he began talking about writing a novel to be called *Springtime for Hitler.*

Yet while other Caesar veterans seemed to be prospering, Brooks's career languished. Then one night he and Carl Reiner went into an ad-lib routine they had been doing at parties for years. Reiner would assign Brooks a character—it might be a pirate or a deaf songwriter—and ask him questions. This night he was the 2,000-Year-Old Man. (Asked by Reiner about his children, Brooks answered in a Yiddish accent, "Forty-two thousand children—and not one comes to visit.")

Steve Allen heard the routine and encouraged Brooks and Reiner to make it into a record. The record came out in 1961, and in four years it and several offshoots had sold more than 10 million copies. Brooks said of his character, "The 2,000-Year-Old Man is a pastiche of everyone around me, my mother, my Uncle Joe, my grandmother. When I became him, I could hear 5,000 years of Jews pouring through me."

With this success, Brooks's personality began to mellow. He became less the wild man of his Sid Caesar days. In 1961, he met and fell in love with the actress Anne Bancroft. After a courtship of three years, they were married, and they now have an eleven-year-old son.

If the pair seems incongruous ("Beauty and the Beast," some friends call them), it is only on the surface. Carl Reiner explains their devotion to each other this way: "They both are sharp and bright and volatile—quick to anger, quick to forgive." Besides, Brooks's private self is different from his public self. "When he's being himself," said the novelist Joseph Heller, a longtime friend, "he'll talk quietly for hours and then make a remark that's un-forgettably funny because it came out of a real situation." He is warm and loving, deeply loyal to his friends, and generous to needy members of his family.

During the 1960s, Brooks had another success—the television series "Get Smart," which he created with another writer. This was a James Bond spoof, with an idiotic secret agent hero (Max-well Smart), who was constantly locking himself in closets and tripping over his own feet. Smart worked for CONTROL, a secret agency of the United States. His enemy was the international agency KAOS. The show was a hit from its first episode (in which the character Mr. Big was played by a dwarf). But it was often criticized for bad taste.

Later, in 1967, when "Get Smart" was well established, Brooks was offered a series of his own, but he turned it down. "TV grinds you up, makes a sausage out of you every week," he said. He ventured back to television only once again, about ten years later, as executive producer and script supervisor for a satirical version of the Robin Hood legend called "When Things Were Rotten." He explained at the time that he "couldn't resist the fun of [a tax collector] saying, 'Hold your tongue,' and [all the peasants] hold-ing their tongues." The show got good reviews at first, but the joke was too limited to be sustained for long.

Mel Brooks got his first taste of moviemaking in 1963, when he conceived, wrote, and narrated *The Critic*. This three-minute film was a satire of the arty, abstract geometric cartoons that were popular at the time. The narrator was a simple old Jewish man sitting in the theater. "Dis is cute, dis is cute, dis is nice," he says. "Vat da hell is it? It must be some symbolism. . . . I think it's symbolic of junk." Brooks shared an Academy Award with his cartoonist for best short subject in the cartoon category.

His first feature-length film, *The Producers*, came four years later. It is the story of a down-and-out theatrical producer, Max Bialystock (played by Zero Mostel), and a timid accountant who deliberately put together a dreadful play *(Springtime for Hitler)*. The play includes girls in a swastika formation singing Brooks's song "Here Comes the Master Race" ("Don't be shtoopid, be a schmarty, come and join the Nazi party"). It is supposed to close as soon as it opens, allowing them to pocket all the money invested in it, but instead it is a smash. The two producers and their star go to jail, where they are last seen rehearsing—and overselling shares in—a new musical, *Prisoners of Love*.

This film was Brooks's way of attacking bigotry and expressing his outrage at the Holocaust. "I think you can bring down totalitarian governments faster," he said, "by using ridicule than you can with invective."

Brooks cast Gene Wilder, who had played opposite his wife in a Brecht play, as the accountant Leo Bloom. Wilder was to become the new vehicle for Brooks's humor as well as his closest friend and most vehement fan. He also became the cornerstone of an informal repertory company, which also included Madeline Kahn, Dom DeLuise, Marty Feldman, Cloris Leachman, and Harvey Korman. Brooks uses the same actors over and over, he has said, because he wants "to surround myself with people I love—make a family."

Brooks fought hard to direct *The Producers* himself, less from the desire to be a film director than in "self-defense." He explains:

"Basically, I'm a writer. I'm the proprietor of the vision. I also know what I eventually want to happen on the screen. So if you have a valuable idea, the only way to protect it is to direct it." In fact, Brooks does much more than that. He takes part in all artistic decisions, including what color the title will be. He also stays with his films through release, supervising every detail of the advertising campaign.

His directing experience at that point, however, was limited to the trailer for one movie. But he was a passionate moviegoer, even as a child ("This was my school—the movies," he has said), and has claimed that "simply seeing movies, you pick up a good deal. I always knew what actors should say to one another and how they should look, and I always understood stage business. That is, should they have a pencil in their hands or be brushing their teeth or peering up a drainpipe when they say, 'I love you.'"

But Brooks's inexperience showed. He himself tells the story of his first day on the set when he dramatically yelled, "Cut!" instead of "Roll 'em!" He also admits that he basically set up the camera and let the actors run around in front of the lens. "I had no idea as to how I would capture the vision that was in my mind on film."

In one respect, though, Brooks was very professional in making *The Producers* and has continued to be in all his films. He finished shooting on schedule and spent only $941,000, which was less than the budget.

Although most critics enjoyed the wild humor of *The Producers*, many considered it too vulgar. Renata Adler summed up the reaction in her review in the *New York Times*, calling it a "violently mixed bag. Some of it is shoddy and gross and cruel; the rest is funny in an entirely unexpected way."

The Producers developed a cult following and was in the black in four years. In addition, Brooks won an Academy Award for best original screenplay.

His next film, *The Twelve Chairs*, took three years to make, including a year of shooting in Yugoslavia. He adapted it from a satiric Russian novel of the 1920s which he had loved as a child. (Brooks is a passionate reader.) It follows three men—a con man, an impoverished aristocrat, and a conniving priest—as they search for twelve dining room chairs in which a fortune in jewels was hidden from the Bolsheviks. "It has all the craziness and *meshugas* that I love," Brooks said, "humanity, greed, destruction, happiness—brush strokes of tenderness. It's the kind of pot I like to stew around in a lot." He wrote the theme song himself— "Hope for the Best/Expect the Worst"—and shot a lot of it "on my belly in the fields."

While the set of *The Producers* had been marked by violent outbursts of temper, the set of this film was harmonious, and Brooks won the admiration of his actors. Today, well-known actors who are not Brooks regulars often seek parts in his films for pure fun and for the experience of working with him.

Although *The Twelve Chairs* was a box office failure and was generally panned, critics agreed that Brooks was outstanding as Tikon, the caretaker of a home for the aged who longs for the good old days of servitude. He recalls his old master: "I loved him. He hardly ever beat us."

Brooks has said that this film "taught me something. There is no room in the business now for a special little picture. You either hit 'em over the head or stay home with the canary." His next four films—all genre satires—hit 'em over the head. The first, *Blazing Saddles*, came to him as a script titled "Tex X" by Andrew Bergman. Since he couldn't stir up any interest in his own projects and because he liked the idea of a modern black man, with double knits and Gucci saddlebags, living in the Old West, he agreed to work on it. But this time he didn't work alone. He went back to the jam session style of his Caesar years and shared the writing with Bergman and three other writers.

Blazing Saddles is about a black sheriff named Bart (Cleavon Little) hired to defend a small town against an evil land-grabbing lawyer, who hopes Bart will be lynched by the bigoted townspeople. Gene Wilder plays the sheriff's sidekick, the Waco Kid, a legendary, quick-draw gunman, now an alcoholic. Madeline Kahn plays Lilli von Shtupp, a bar singer who talks like Marlene Dietrich with a speech impediment. She even writes that way. "I must see you wight away," says her note to Bart. "Please come to my dwessing woom." Brooks himself plays two roles—the corrupt, lecherous governor Lepetomain and a Yiddish-speaking Indian chief.

The film is a mixture of satire, parody, farce, and bathroom humor. It ends with a painted cardboard model of the town and its citizens, built as an ambush for the bad guys. Their battle overflows onto a real Hollywood set where a musical is being rehearsed. Finally, Bart and Waco ride into the sunset, only to abandon their horses for a chauffered limousine, Brooks's last laugh at the movie version of the West.

Brooks said of *Blazing Saddles*, "I figured my career was finished anyway, so I wrote berserk, heartfelt stuff about white corruption and racism and Bible-thumping bigotry. We used dirty language on the screen for the first time, and to me the whole thing was like a big psychoanalytic session. I just got everything out of me—all my furor, my frenzy, my insanity, my love of life, and my hatred of death."

He had no idea it would be a box office hit. In fact, at the first screening, for Warners executives, there was hardly a laugh, even at the scene where a chain gang boss tells his prisoners to sing a typical black work song and they break into Cole Porter's "I Get a Kick Out of You." Later that night, in a room filled with all the other Warners employees, there were roars. Thus was born Brooks's tradition of doing his screenings before a large, diverse audience.

The film was accused of being chaotic, but Brooks denies the charge. "It was calculated chaos," he said. "I'm a very well-trained maniac." Brooks has said that he takes two years to make a picture—eighteen months for writing and six for production. "I write and rewrite for the kind of comedy I do, keep pads and pencils all over the house, jotting down new lines and dialogue that comes to mind any time of day or night."

He also claims that every scene and almost every line of his films is in the script. "You can improvise with rhythms and motions during rehearsals," he said, "but not with lines." He has a three-week preparation period before shooting. "I take the crew, and we meet every day and go from page one to page one hundred twenty. Every department raises their hand and says, 'What do we do here?' I'm very organized, so that we know every day exactly what we should accomplish, and what is needed to accomplish it, both artistically and technically. We plan every move, every camera angle. . . ."

While they were finishing *Blazing Saddles*, Gene Wilder came up with the idea for *Young Frankenstein*. He wrote the first draft, and Brooks revised it. 20th Century-Fox gave them $2.8 million and has remained loyal to Brooks ever since. He always has final cut, a guarantee that the studio won't change the film once he is done with it.

Young Frankenstein is the story of the great-grandson of Dr. Beaufort Frankenstein. Young Frederick is a modern brain surgeon who returns to the ancestral estate and is seduced by the idea of creating a man. Wilder played Young Frankenstein and Marty Feldman was the hunchback assistant Igor, whose hump keeps switching sides. Madeline Kahn played Young Frankenstein's frigid fiancée. They rub elbows good-bye so that he won't muss up her makeup, clothes, or hairdo. Her sexuality is finally excited by "old zipper-neck," as she calls the monster. In the film's happy ending, Frankenstein arranges to share some of his intellectual endowment with the monster in exchange for some of the monster's sexual prowess.

Brooks described *Young Frankenstein* as his first attempt at half laughs and half story, resulting in a more straightforward plot. The film was very successful at the box office. It also got better reviews than any Brooks film before, and it received several raves.

He was praised for his camera work and his fastidious attention to detail. Brooks did a lot of research so that everything in the film, right down to the acting, could be done in 1930s style. "We wanted to make a hilarious pastiche of the old black-and-white horror films of the thirties," he said, and "we wanted to offer sincere and reverent homage to those same beautifully made movies." *Young Frankenstein* was shot in black-and-white, and Brooks used techniques of the thirties like sudden closeups and cuts, halos around the heads, and swirling fog around the castle. Half of the scientific machinery came from the sets of old Frankenstein films.

Brooks paid vigilant attention to pacing and nuance. He directs with an eye to editing, always aware of both ends of a joke, and he is very careful. There is a four-minute scene between the monster and a lonely blind man (Gene Hackman), who thinks he has a longed-for visitor. It is filled with slapstick humor, as he pours soup on the monster's lap, smashes his glass in a toast, and lights his thumb instead of a cigar. This scene took four days (from 6:00 A.M. to 9:00 P.M.) to shoot to Brooks's satisfaction.

Brooks also worked very closely with the editor, going through the film frame by frame at least twelve times. The decision as to where and when to cut was usually Brooks's. He has said that editing is like rewriting, and has described the way he works: "My principle of cutting is you start with a scalpel and end with a blunt ax. Everyone usually does it the other way around. You know, knocking out whole scenes and ending by refining. But I start by taking out an 'and,' an 'if,' or a 'but.' I play with a scene. Then when you have the rough cut, you start eliminating scenes."

As a filmmaker, Mel Brooks is of two minds about his art. On the one hand, he has said, "I'm trying to get back to . . . the golden age of comedy with Laurel and Hardy, with Chaplin, with

Buster Keaton, just flat-out smash belly-comedy." On the other hand, he often attributes serious themes to his films, and he has said that he needs a "philosophical base" in his comedy. *The Producers* and *Blazing Saddles* are about bigotry, and he has said that *Young Frankenstein* is about man's dream of being a god and about what he calls "womb envy."

Brooks described his next movie (and next hit)—*Silent Movie*—as an "experimental" film. It was a joint project with a group of writers who stayed together for another film also. In *Silent Movie*, Mel Funn (Brooks), a washed-up, reformed alcoholic Hollywood director, tries to save his studio from takeover by the conglomerate Engulf and Devour by making a silent film. He is assisted by Marty Eggs (Feldman) and Dom Bell (DeLuise).

"It was very difficult for me," he said. "because all my training has been vocal. . . . So I did *Silent Movie* as a kind of punishment, as a task, as an exercise to expand my visual muscles." Although this movie has very noisy sound effects, there is no dialogue except the single word "no," spoken by the mime Marcel Marceau.

Silent Movie gave Brooks his first leading role. When Gene Wilder wasn't available, Brooks himself decided to play the part of Funn. But he worried about it. "One of the requirements of a film," said the stocky comic with rubbery features, "is to deliver nice-looking people to the audience."

With one success as a star and with Wilder still unavailable, Brooks gave himself the leading role in his next film, *High Anxiety*. This Hitchcock spoof is the story of Dr. Richard H. Thorndyke, a psychiatrist with a fear of heights, who is appointed to head the Psycho-Neurotic Institute for the Very, *Very* Nervous. He must take control away from greedy evildoers. The rate of recovery at the expensive clinic, the assistant director figures out on his pocket calculator, is "once in a blue moon." Unfortunately, the institute is located on top of a hill.

Brooks called the film "an homage to Hitchcock, who has been

Mel Brooks as the director of *High Anxiety*. PHOTO: Courtesy of 20th Century-Fox

my favorite director since I was five years old." His research included seeing every Hitchcock film at least a dozen times, and he even went to the master for his blessing. Brooks tried to make *High Anxiety* look like a Hitchcock film, and it makes many references to his work, including a scene of birds (pigeons rather than bloodthirsty crows) attacking with mayonnaise and spinach droppings.

He also used a scene from *The Lodger*, which had haunted him since he was a child. In that film the camera shoots a man walking on a glass floor from below; in *High Anxiety* the camera is under a glass coffee table. At a critical moment, a coffee pot is put down, obscuring the view. "The camera gets frantic," he said. "Finally the lens is wiped out with a tray of strudel."

Another target for spoof in the film is psychiatry itself. Thorndyke explains, for instance, that he once considered a singing career, but "the big bucks are in psychiatry. I mean, it's so much more emotionally involving."

Again Brooks worked very carefully, keeping his three cowriters on the set as continual advisers, scrutinizing video replays of each take with the actors.

Some critics called the film uneven and vulgar, but Brooks's audience paid more than $20 million to see it in the first year.

His most recent film, *History of the World—Part I*, is made up of six historical sketches. Brooks was producer, director, writer, and star. He played Louis XVI; a dancing, singing Torquemada; and Comicus, a stand-up philosopher who is out of work and settles for a job as a waiter. (At the Last Supper, he asks, "Are you all together or is it separate checks?")

Although many of the criticisms were the same as always, Vincent Canby in the *New York Times* wrote that, in his opinion, this film "redefines and clarifies" the comic methods of the others. "The point of Mr. Brooks's use of foul language, obscene gestures, a preoccupation with bodily functions and with sex as the single most overwhelmingly human impulse is to remind us that we may not be quite as civilized as is otherwise indicated."

In the immediate future, a sequel to *History of the World* seems inevitable. The film even ends with "Coming Attractions" (including "Jews in Space"). It is also likely that, having laid out his territory of wild, low comedy, Brooks will not abandon it or his huge audience. "It's one of the great joys of my life," he has said, "to walk down the aisle toward the screen, spin around and slowly walk back up while the audience is laughing at my work."

Francis Coppola

Francis Coppola

Dementia 13 (1963)
You're a Big Boy Now (1967)
Finian's Rainbow (1968)
The Rain People (1969)
The Godfather (1972)
The Conversation (1974)
The Godfather—Part II (1974)
Apocalypse Now (1979)
One from the Heart (1982)
The Outsiders (1983)

THE CAREER OF FRANCIS COPPOLA heads in two different directions at once. Part of him aims to be a serious film artist, the other part wants to be a rich and powerful movie mogul. Because of his ambition to combine the two (and perhaps also because of his ample waistline and bushy beard), he has been compared with Orson Welles.

Coppola's instinct for showmanship did not really surface until college. He was born on April 7, 1939, in Detroit, the second of three children of Italia and Carmine Coppola. He has described himself as a child as "funny-looking, not good in school, near-sighted," an unpopular kid "immersed in a fantasy world." He was nicknamed "Science" at school because he was always tinkering with gadgets.

51

His younger sister is the actress Talia Shire, who played Connie Corleone in *The Godfather* (and was actually hired for the film before Francis was). His older brother August is a writer and college English professor, who ran an educational and apprenticeship program for Francis's Zoetrope Studios. Francis grew up viewing August as "handsomer, brilliant, the adored one of any group."

Although the Coppolas lived a suburban middle-class life, it was not an entirely sunny one. The family moved about thirty times as Carmine, a flutist, conductor, and composer, searched for conducting jobs. "Our lives centered on what we all felt was the tragedy of his career," according to Francis. "He was a very talented man . . . he felt that his own music never really emerged." As soon as he had the power, Coppola hired his father to work on his productions—from college plays to his first films. Finally, Carmine Coppola won an Oscar, shared with the famous composer Nino Rota, for the score of *The Godfather—Part II*. "That moment was so great," his son has said, "I really didn't care whether I got an Oscar or not."

At the age of nine, Francis Coppola began his theatrical career. He had developed polio (like Harry Caul in *The Conversation*) and was confined to bed for a year. For company he had a 16-millimeter movie projector, a tape recorder, a record player, a television set, a ventriloquist's dummy, and comic books. ("They're just like screenplays.") He put on puppet shows regularly and created sound tracks for the silent movies he showed on his bedroom wall.

When he was fourteen, he made his first film by cutting up the family's home movies to recast himself as the hero. He edited them into features with titles like *The Rich Millionaire* and *The Lost Wallet*. At a military high school he attended briefly, Coppola wrote the book and lyrics for the class musical. He also wrote love letters for fellow cadets, charging them a dollar a page.

He graduated from high school in Great Neck, a suburb of

New York where his parents finally settled, and went on to Hofstra University on Long Island, on a drama scholarship. After seeing Sergei Eisenstein's *Ten Days That Shook the World*, he had decided to become a filmmaker. But he wanted to model his career after that of the Russian director and study theater first.

At Hofstra, Coppola was a big man on campus. He wrote for and edited the student literary magazine; he directed plays, including a musical, which he staged with a thirty-piece professional orchestra; and he wrote the book and lyrics for an original musical comedy. He won three awards for theatrical direction and production. He also took a stab at filmmaking. In his junior year he sold his car to buy a 16-millimeter camera. But he didn't finish the movie he tried to make because, he said, "I just didn't have the technical expertise."

Perhaps Coppola's greatest accomplishment, however, and the signpost for the future was managing to merge the school's drama group and musical comedy club, thus gaining control of a $30,000 yearly budget.

After he graduated in 1959, Coppola went, as planned, to film school at UCLA. But he found it disappointing. The students were all pessimistic about ever being able to succeed in Hollywood without compromising their art. While they sat around bemoaning their fate, Coppola was making movies. For small fees, he directed some "very innocent" sex films with titles like *The Peeper, Tonight for Sure*, and *The Belt Girls and the Playboy*.

It was through these that he got his education: "You do everything yourself, from first script to final editing. . . . You learn the fullest use to which each element in moviemaking can be put . . . and you learn how to make the most out of every dollar in the budget."

He also became an assistant to Roger Corman, king of the low-budget horror film. His first assignment, though he knew no Russian, was to write an English script for a Russian science fiction film and turn it into a monster movie. He worked on four more Corman films as sound man, dialogue director, and associate producer, and then was rewarded with a horror picture of his own.

In three and a half days Coppola wrote the script for *Dementia 13*, the story of a doomed family, which includes the required number of ax murders. Corman gave him $20,000 and a cast and crew already on location in Ireland. (The art director of *Dementia 13* was Eleanor Neil, a graphic artist who is now Coppola's wife and the mother of his three children.) Coppola, typically, managed to obtain another $20,000 for his film by selling British rights. *Dementia 13* got some kind reviews but many negative ones.

Coppola won first prize in the Samuel Goldwyn writing competition in 1962 for a screenplay titled *Pilma, Pilma*. Although it has never been produced, it gave him an entrée to Hollywood—as a staff writer for Seven Arts, a company that put together films for major studios. He wrote ten or twelve screenplays in two years, but the few that reached the screen bore little resemblance to what he had written. And still he couldn't persuade anyone to let him direct. "In fact," he has said, "I wrote a screenplay about a guy who wants to direct a movie so bad he goes crazy, just to put my position more strongly across."

Coppola took his first big gamble with $20,000 he had saved from his salary. He invested it all in the stock market, hoping to turn it into enough money to make a movie. Instead, he lost his entire investment.

Meanwhile his reputation as a writer was growing, and 20th Century-Fox hired him to write a screenplay about World War II General George Patton. His script, which portrayed the general as "a man out of his time, a pathetic hero, a Don Quixote figure," was scrapped by the studio. But later George C. Scott, who eventually starred in the movie, resurrected it, and in 1970 Francis Coppola won his first Oscar as coauthor of the screenplay for *Patton*.

While he was still working for Seven Arts by day, Coppola had spent his nights writing a screenplay based on an English novel titled *You're a Big Boy Now*, for which he owned the rights. He sold the rights to Seven Arts and was finally hired as a director. The film is a farce about an adolescent boy who takes a job in the New York Public Library and tries to overcome his shyness and fear of girls. It was one of the first films to use rock music for its score.

With his charm and audacity, Coppola managed to persuade New York Mayor John V. Lindsay to allow him to film the star (Peter Kastner) roller-skating through the stacks of the solemn library. He also persuaded three prominent stars who had never heard of him before—Rip Torn, Geraldine Page, and Julie Harris—to appear in the film.

Although many reviewers found the humor in the film too absurd, his talent—especially his sensitive use of actors—was generally acknowledged. The film, whose budget grew from $250,000 to $1 million, lost money, but it accomplished two purposes for Coppola: it earned him his master's degree from UCLA and, more important, it drew attention to him as a director.

Coppola was already fascinated by the new technology available to filmmakers. He made a videotape of the actors performing a separate rehearsal script he wrote for *Big Boy*, which he then studied. This gave the actors a chance to develop their parts and the director a sense of what his picture was going to be like before he even began shooting.

The next picture Coppola took on—*Finian's Rainbow*, a Hollywood musical based on the 1940s Broadway show—brought accusations that he was selling out. The film is about a leprechaun with a crock of gold that grants wishes and is used to turn a white senator black. Coppola had decided to write his own screenplay based on the original book rather than use a topical adapation. Unfortunately, he wasn't done writing when shooting had to begin, and the material was too dated anyway. Other problems beyond his control, including a miscast leprechaun and a bad choreographer, helped to make the film a gigantic flop.

Before the extent of this fiasco was apparent, Warner Brothers offered Coppola $400,000 to direct *Mame*, another musical. But he turned it down in order to make *The Rain People*, a personal film based on a story he had written in college. With the money he had earned from *Finian*, he bought a van and $80,000 worth of equipment, including a complex editing machine that gave him the ability to edit as he went along.

Then he got Warner Brothers to invest in the film, which is about a pregnant woman who leaves her husband and her responsibilities one rainy morning and drives west, befriending a brain-damaged football player on the way. According to Coppola, it "rests on the idea of human responsibility—what we owe each other, what we owe ourselves."

A seventeen-member crew in seven vehicles made that pilgrimage with the main character for four months across eighteen states. Before they left, Coppola rehearsed the cast for three weeks with a special script written for the stage.

Although Coppola was writing as they went along and would incorporate interesting things they saw, the style of the film, he has said, "was not that of improvisation. But we hoped to get the flavor of improvisation. The basis was scripted, thought out— and, hopefully, is thematically whole."

The film was a financial failure, and the reviews were generally lukewarm, criticizing the plot, the pace, and the inconclusive ending, but usually praising the actors' performances.

In 1969, before *The Rain People* was released, Coppola had already organized from the crew of that film the core of what was to be his own company. American Zoetrope was named after a nineteenth-century device, a revolving drum with slits in it, which created the first motion picture. Thus really began the second branch of his career—as a movie mogul.

American Zoetrope was located on three floors of a converted warehouse in downtown San Francisco. It had editing rooms, screening rooms, and the newest, most advanced equipment—everything needed to make movies except a sound stage. There were twelve to fifteen staff members and eight filmmakers. "What we're really doing," Coppola said at the time, "is giving these young filmmakers a chance to make films." But the company was also, he said, "a true capitalist venture, designed to sustain itself and provide artistic freedom through money." He got Warner Brothers to invest $3.5 million.

Unfortunately, after six months Warners didn't like what it saw and withdrew its money, leaving Coppola with his equipment and his facility and half a million dollars in debt. When Paramount asked him to direct and coauthor the screenplay for the movie version of the best-selling novel *The Godfather*, it was, as the line in the movie goes, "an offer he couldn't refuse."

This is the story of a Mafia family, the Corleones, from the end of World War II to the mid-1950s, when the power passes from father to son. Originally slated as a conventional gangster movie, the three-hour epic grossed about $300 million worldwide and won three Academy Awards—for best picture, best actor, and best screenplay based on another medium. Jay Cocks, the *Time* magazine critic, wrote of *The Godfather*: "In its blending of new depth with an old genre, it becomes that rarity, a mass entertainment that is also great movie art."

Cocks also wrote that "no American film before *The Godfather* has caught so truly the texture of an ethnic subculture." Coppola drew from his memories of family rituals authentic and colorful details for the wedding at the beginning of the film and the christening at the end. Even so simple a detail as a man entering his mother's kitchen and, before anything else, dipping a piece of bread in the pot simmering on the stove rings true of Italian-American life.

The major criticism of the film was that it romanticized the Mafia, that criminals were portrayed as adventurers. But Coppola said in answer, "I felt it was making a harsh statement about the Mafia and power at the end of *Godfather I* when Michael [the new Godfather] murders all those people, then lies to his wife and closes the door." He also said that the Mafia is a metaphor for America. The first line of the film, he pointed out, is "I believe in America."

The violence in this world is made explicit. People are shot, strangled, and blown up in cars. In one particularly gruesome episode, a movie company executive who was not cooperating with the mob finds the bloody head of his prize horse on his bed.

The filming itself was not all easy sailing. As the budget soared from $1 million to over $5 million, the studio began to get worried and, according to Coppola, "I was getting 'fired' every other week. The things they were going to fire me over were . . . wanting to cast Brando [as Don Vito, the Godfather], wanting to cast Pacino [as Michael], wanting to shoot in Sicily, wanting to make it in period. The very things that made the film different from any other film."

The crew members and actors also feared that the young director didn't know what he was doing. Coppola always shoots scenes over and over until he gets an actor's best performance. As a result, his rough cuts (before editing) always look dreadful. "What you select in editing is part of the writing process," he has said. "It was in the post-production for Part I that I found what we had—those performances from Brando and Pacino that knit the film together."

In fact, it was the actors' performances that again brought Coppola the greatest praise. He used one unusual technique before shooting began. He gave a dinner for the cast at which he asked them to improvise. They naturally began to act like a family, all competing for Brando's attention. On the set, though, he has said, "I may sometimes get my actors to improvise, but it is always within a framework and to make a point that I have decided on. After all, I am the only one who can know how the whole film is going to shape and precisely what the function of any particular piece will be."

Between *The Godfather* and the inevitable sequel, Coppola directed a play and an opera in San Francisco. He said that he needed to do something different, "something where I could experiment more freely, without political or financial pressures."

During that time, he also wrote the screenplay for *The Great Gatsby*, directed by Jack Clayton, which generally got poor reviews. Before this, Coppola had thought of himself mainly as a writer and of writing as "the primary act of creation." Afterwards, however, he said, "I was so impressed by how badly *Gatsby* worked that I started to put more credit to what a director does."

After *The Godfather*, Paramount formed the jointly owned Directors Company, with Coppola, Peter Bogdanovich, and William Friedkin, the three major directors of the day. The studio had agreed to finance and distribute their films, but the deal fell through after only three were made. One of these was *The Conversation*, which Coppola wrote and directed. He chose this personal film, costing less than $2 million, he said, because "at that point in my career the most important thing was to confirm to myself that I could do original work."

The Conversation is a psychological thriller about a professional wiretapper, Harry Caul ("the best bugger on the West Coast"). Although he is compulsively private himself (his own girl friend doesn't know what he does or how to reach him), he becomes emotionally involved in an assignment. He overhears a sentence, "He'd kill us if he got the chance," on a tape he was hired to make and is convinced that an attractive young couple are going to be murdered. Haunted by another assignment that led to deaths, he tries to withhold the tapes. "I wasn't making a film about *privacy*, as I had set out to do," Coppola said, "but rather, once again, a film about *responsibility*, as was *The Rain People*."

He used the camera and the sound track to give the audience

the sense of eavesdropping on Harry's personal life. The very static camera "gave the impression that it didn't have an operator on it," he said, "so that the actor would walk out of the frame, just as if it were an electronic camera." He also tried to make the sound track from Harry's point of view: "I wrote many scenes to be sound-oriented like a murder occurring in another room that you don't see but you hear."

The film was very well received by critics. Stephen Farber in the *New York Times* called it "Coppola's best movie, a landmark film of the seventies, and a stunning piece of original American fiction. It also won the highest award at the Cannes Film Festival. But it was not popular at the box office.

While he was still editing *The Conversation*, Coppola was frantically writing and shooting *The Godfather—Part II*. To the reporters who kept asking him why he agreed to do this sequel, Coppola gave a number of answers. Among them were the challenge this time of being allowed to do whatever he wanted and the desire to make a statement about power by linking Michael Corleone directly to big business and corrupt politicians. "And to be completely honest," he told one reporter, "there was the possibility of my making so much money I could bankroll some of my other projects."

That is exactly what happened. Coppola reportedly got 15 percent of the film's gross profits. In addition, though, *The Godfather—Part II* is considered by many critics to be the most significant American film of the decade. It won six Oscars, including those for best picture, best director, best screenplay, and best original dramatic score.

The film, which is twenty-five minutes longer than *The Godfather*, juxtaposes the fall of Michael, the new Godfather, with flashbacks of his father's rise a half-century earlier. Young Vito is seen at the turn of the century fleeing Sicily, where his parents and older brother were killed. In New York, Vito (played by Robert De Niro) avenges their deaths and rises to power in the neighborhood, partly by protecting the weak. Meanwhile, Michael's main concern is gaining greater control of Las Vegas gambling. He becomes a less and less attractive figure and by the end of the film is all alone, betrayed by his brother and abandoned by his wife.

Ironically, the film's structure, which has been especially praised, was a last-minute decision made just weeks before it was released. For a long time Coppola worried that he had two different films, shot in different styles, with "a different smell to them." He crowded friends and associates into the editing rooms, using their reactions to help sort this out.

In 1975, Francis Coppola's personal fortune included a legitimate theater, a radio station, and large real-estate holdings. To this he added a large investment in a film distribution company and in *City*, a San Francisco–based magazine, which he attempted unsuccessfully to publish and edit. *City* folded in early 1976, just as Coppola left for the Philippines to begin filming *Apocalypse Now*.

This film about the Vietnam War uses as its framework Joseph Conrad's novel *Heart of Darkness*. An army captain named Willard (Martin Sheen) is assigned to "terminate with extreme prejudice" the command of Colonel Kurtz (Marlon Brando), who has gone mad and become emperor of a band of Cambodian natives deep in the jungle. Willard's long boat ride up the river to this quarry highlights many of the horrors of war. In one bizarre scene, a lieutenant orders a village strafed to clear the water for a famous surfer traveling with Willard.

Coppola spent almost four years and $30 million making this controversial film. The emotional strain nearly cost him his marriage. And because no studio would support the project financially, he had to do it himself. The filming was plagued by discomfort and misfortune. There was unbearable heat and persistent rain. The cast and crew suffered from dysentery. A typhoon destroyed $1 million worth of sets, and Martin Sheen had a heart attack three-quarters of the way through filming. "There were times," Coppola said later, "when I thought I was going to die, literally, from the inability to move the problems I had."

The original script for the film was written by John Milius almost ten years earlier as one of the American Zoetrope projects Warner Brothers turned its back on. But it was not what Coppola wanted—it didn't have enough of the Conrad novel in it—so he decided to rewrite it himself. He had a list of two hundred points he wanted to make about the war, including the fact that the use of drugs was widespread, that many of the soldiers were naive seventeen-year-olds, that most of them were black, and that the top officers were living extravagantly.

Early in the morning, he would sit in his houseboat writing the script on index cards. At night he would review videocassettes of the film. When Marlon Brandon arrived to play Kurtz, his part wasn't ready. He and Coppola together worked out various versions of his important monologue and taped them.

Coppola shot a million feet of film during the sixteen months of filming and then spent two years trying to shape it. He boldly previewed the film in Los Angeles in 1979, passing out a sealed questionnaire that was "my invitation to you to help me finish the film." He also entered it in the Cannes Film Festival as "work in progress" because he still hadn't settled on an ending. That gamble paid off. The film shared the grand prize.

Coppola said of *Apocalypse Now*, "I tried to make it more of an experience than a movie." He used no documentary footage: "Every shot in that film was shot on a long dolly and was very operatic and lyrical. I used red and orange smoke right from the beginning to tell you it was all an opera."

The film got generally good reviews, and his rendering of the war in the first two-thirds was praised. But many critics found the meeting between Willard and Kurtz, who quotes T. S. Eliot, "pretentious" and not worthy of comparison with Conrad.

By 1981, when the film broke even, Coppola had already

expanded his empire. The year before, he had bought the Hollywood General Studio, built in 1919, for $6.7 million. He now had ten acres in the heart of Hollywood and a facility with nine sound stages, projection rooms, thirty-four editing rooms, and a special effects shop. Zoetrope Studios was born. Here he planned to create an updated version of the studio system of the 1930s— actors and writers under contract, senior filmmakers on tap, "a family of people working together from inception to final product." He also planned to develop what he calls electronic cinema, the use of computer and video equipment in filmmaking.

Zoetrope put its stamp on three films: *The Escape Artist*, directed by Caleb Deschanel; *Hammett*, directed by Wim Wenders, but shelved indefinitely; and Coppola's own film *One from the Heart*. The studio also began to distribute films of foreign directors in this country.

But almost immediately there were crises. The budget of *One from the Heart* soared from $15 million to $27 million, and investors pulled out. Coppola was saved only by last-minute loans and a staff willing to work for half-pay. But the film itself did poorly at the box office, leaving him in financial trouble.

One from the Heart is a love story. An ordinary couple—she is a travel agent and he owns a wrecking company—fight and break up on the eve of the anniversary of their meeting. They both go to Las Vegas for the Fourth of July weekend and meet romantic lovers. Hers is a Latin waiter and singer (Raul Julia); his is a circus acrobat (Nastassia Kinski). But they are drawn back together for a happy ending.

At great cost, Coppola recreated Las Vegas on the Zoetrope lot. He wanted to give the film a magical, unreal quality. After the experience of *Apocalypse Now*, he also wanted to be in complete control. And he was. Before shooting even began, he was able to see the whole film. He videotaped artists' sketches of more than five hundred scenes and recorded the actors reading a radio play version of the script. He directed the film from a silver trailer

Coppola on the set of *One from the Heart*.

(dubbed Image Control), which held a computer, TV monitors, microphones, and telephones. He could see exactly what the camera lens was focusing on and could adjust and edit each sequence as it was shot.

Reviews of the film ranged from the lukewarm, questioning whether the love story was strong enough to support the technological splendor of the production, to the harsh. David Ansen wrote in *Newsweek*, "What happens is that the style overwhelms everything. The audience literally applauds the sets but loses sight of the characters."

Nevertheless, Coppola insists that it is "probably the most interesting movie I've ever made." He and his electronic cinema quickly moved on to Tulsa, where he began shooting two films based on teenage novels by S. E. Hinton—*The Outsiders* and *Rumble Fish*.

In February 1983, Zoetrope Studios was living on a bank loan, which Coppola was struggling to pay, and the bank was losing patience. Since his personal finances are tied closely to the company, it is not surprising that his home telephone was turned off for a year because he could not pay the bill. Yet Francis Coppola remains undaunted. "You can't be an artist and be safe," he said recently.

Brian De Palma (center) with John Travolta and Nancy Allen on the set of *Blow Out*. PHOTO: United Press International

Brian De Palma

The Wedding Party (1964)	*Phantom of the Paradise* (1974)
Murder à la Mod (1968)	*Obsession* (1976)
Greetings (1968)	*Carrie* (1976)
Hi, Mom! (1970)	*The Fury* (1978)
Dionysus in '69 (1970)	*Home Movies* (1980)
Get to Know Your Rabbit (1970)	*Dressed to Kill* (1980)
Sisters (1973)	*Blow Out* (1981)

SOME REVIEWERS HAIL Brian De Palma as Master of the Macabre, Prince of Terror, Merchant of Menace, and the Hitchcock of the Seventies. Others call him a cheap imitator and a cold technician who uses blood and violence to manipulate his audiences. De Palma sees himself as a serious filmmaker striving for "the ultimate in filmmaking." He looks at his own films critically again and again, "just to remind myself what was wrong with them. . . . It makes me very aware of what I have to do to grow as a director." And he feels very strongly about his artistic integrity. "I'm devoted to what I'm making," he has said; "what I *am* is up there on the screen."

But Brian De Palma did not always want to direct films. Until he was in college, his "work-oriented, success-oriented" parents were pushing their scientifically inclined son to become a doctor. Meanwhile, his own heart's dream was to go to the moon.

De Palma was born on September 11, 1940, in Newark, New Jersey, and grew up in Philadelphia, where his family moved when he was six. He was the youngest of three sons of a politically conservative orthopedic surgeon. De Palma often traces his high tolerance for blood and gore in his films to watching his father in the operating theater as a young boy. He saw him cut open bodies and amputate limbs. When he was seventeen he even did bone transplants himself on animals in his father's lab.

In high school he won second prize at a national science fair and during his senior year designed and built a computer just like the one built by the computer whiz kid in *Dressed to Kill*. He has said, in fact, that "that character in *Dressed to Kill* is me."

De Palma attributes his method of moviemaking—working in a "precise, well-thought-out manner"—in part to his scientific background. He plans his movies shot by shot in advance, including details of camera angle and lighting. "Every shot," he has said, "has a conception behind it." He makes sketches of the scenes and sometimes even takes photographs, then tacks them up around his office. He then moves them around and thinks about them for months, until every scene and every image works in relation to the others. The reason he rejected medicine as a career was that it wasn't "precise enough for me. There seemed to be too much conjecture, too much human error."

At Columbia College, in New York City, he started out majoring in physics (one of his older brothers was a physicist), but he switched to fine arts. He had acted in high school and became involved in college theater as an extracurricular activity. He also became "obsessed" by movies, especially certain movies by Roman Polanski and Alfred Hitchcock. "They seemed terrifying and wonderful to me, and suddenly I knew that I could convey my dreams on the screen. No other art form would do."

He began hanging around the graduate film department and bought himself a secondhand camera. With money from his allowance and from selling everything he owned, including his scientific equipment, he managed to make several short films. The first two of these he describes as "pretentious." But *Wotan's Wake*, a twenty-eight-minute mock horror film he made in his senior year, won every award for a short film that year.

With this recognition, De Palma won a graduate writing fellowship to Sarah Lawrence College. While he was there working on his master's degree and taking a film production course at New York University, he produced, wrote, directed, and edited his first feature, *The Wedding Party*. This satirical film, based on his best friend's wedding, is about the prospective bridegroom's stay at his fiancée's family mansion just before the wedding, and his attempt to escape. It is notable for two things: it is filled with experimental camera and editing techniques that De Palma continues to use—jump cuts, improvised scenes, fast forward, and slow motion; and it starred two new actors—Robert De Niro and Jill Clayburgh.

But it did not bring him even near commercial success. That would take eight more feature films and more than ten years. His first five films were made in New York independently and inexpensively (for $100,000 or less).

When he left Sarah Lawrence, De Palma supported himself by making documentaries for clients including the Museum of Modern Art, the NAACP, and the Treasury Department (*Show Me a Strong Town and I'll Show You a Strong Bank*). He earned enough money to finance *Murder à la Mod*, which he directed, wrote, and edited himself. This is a murder story told from the points of view of three characters, reflected by three different film styles. Seen through the eyes of a deaf-mute character, for instance, the story is a silent comedy. In typical self-criticism, De Palma said several years later, "It didn't work because nobody cared about the characters, and the story was so complicated."

His next two films, *Greetings* and *Hi, Mom!*, were "youth

films," attacking establishment targets. De Palma describes them
as statements "of what was going on in my life and the lives
around me at that period." He made *Greetings* while he was in a
"new talent" program run by Universal Studios. He was hired to
write, he said, but nobody read the scripts he sent in. The admin-
istrator of the program, who was equally frustrated, wrote the
script for *Greetings* with him and raised the money to produce it.
They shot it in two weeks with a crew of eight friends, relatives,
and film students. The film, which takes its title from the saluta-
tion on draft notices, follows three boys around the country—a
draft dodger, a Kennedy assassination buff, and a porno artist/
filmmaker (Robert De Niro).

Although many critics found the satire "unfunny," it won De
Palma a Silver Bear Award in Berlin and made more than $1
million. It also was his first film to be distributed nationally, and
De Palma was taken up by the media for a while. But he soon
began to feel that he was being used. "I found myself a guest on
the 'Joe Franklin Show,' talking about revolution and nudity, and
nobody cared about what I said. I was filling up space to sell
headache pills."

Hi, Mom! was a kind of sequel, with Robert De Niro returning
from the Vietnam War. It made fun of white liberals, black
militants, and voyeuristic moviemakers. Critics generally found it
sharper and funnier than *Greetings*, but the film didn't do well at
the box office. De Palma criticizes it for being "too unintegrated
. . . so loose that we had to find a shape for it in the editing
room."

While he was finishing *Hi, Mom!*, De Palma filmed an en-
vironmental theater production called *Dionysus in '69*, which
was based on Euripides' *The Bacchae*. He financed it himself
because he was "floored by the emotional power of it" and
thought it should be preserved. To do that, he conceived and
edited it entirely as a split screen, a technique he has made his

own. One side showed the play, the other the reaction and involvement of the audience. The film was praised but made no money.

Editing that split screen took De Palma about a year, and *Dionysus in '69* was the last film he edited alone. He likes to have an editor put together the film as it is being shot so that he can add any missing pieces. He also likes to get another person's responses. Since De Palma's films are so thoroughly planned, he is losing very little personal control. He usually works with the same editor, Paul Hirsch. "As we progress from picture to picture, he almost knows exactly what I have in mind," De Palma has said. "When he gets the footage back, he knows my storyboards and lays it out just like that."

In spite of his feelings about the establishment and his experience with the media, De Palma said after *Hi, Mom!*, "I don't want to make $100,000 movies in back rooms all my life. I'm interested in making my work as good as possible, and if I can put myself into a really heavyweight situation, I'm going to do it."

His reputation as a director with a savage sense of humor finally got him his first shot at Hollywood—one that set him back six years and created permanent feelings of bitterness and suspicion. Warner Brothers hired De Palma to direct *Get to Know Your Rabbit*, the film debut of the comedian Tom Smothers. The film is about a computer executive who drops out to become a tap-dancing magician. De Palma began to have trouble with his star because Smothers didn't like the character he played. Smothers wanted him to be more aggressive, and he was the one who had the influence with the studio. De Palma finally walked away from the picture when Smothers refused to reshoot some scenes. The film was delayed for two years while a Warners executive edited it, and then it flopped.

"I learned from my *Rabbit* experience that you have to be in complete control of a situation," De Palma has said. Meanwhile,

Hollywood had learned that he was a "difficult" director, and he was out of work for a year, until he got independent financing for *Sisters*.

De Palma's next three films—*Sisters, Phantom of the Paradise*, and *Obsession*—were all low-budget (about $1.5 million) independent productions, and none of them received very good reviews. But they moved him into the horror/suspense genre where he was ultimately to be most successful. "The reason I like the genre," he has said, "is because you can work in a sort of pure cinematic form. That is why Hitchcock likes it, too. It's all images, and your storytelling is entirely through images and not people talking to each other." He has described his craft as "scaring people with films that are both amusing and more and more visual."

Sisters is the story of Siamese twins, a murder, and a girl reporter who becomes involved. Almost eight years earlier De Palma had seen a photograph in *Life* magazine of a pair of Russian Siamese twins, one smiling, one scowling. "This strong visual image started the whole idea in my mind." His twist is that the sweet sister and the vicious sister turn out to be the same person. When they are separated, one twin dies and the other incorporates her personality.

Although *Sisters* grossed more than $4 million, De Palma had really made it for himself, in order to "develop as a director." "Most of my movies before were sort of cold, intellectual, and satiric," he has said, "and certain parts were good, but there was no structure. . . . This movie was a conscious attempt to tell a story, to involve the audience with the characters, to work in a very cinematic style."

Sisters was the first film for which De Palma was accused of borrowing from Alfred Hitchcock, especially from *Rear Window*. In both films, a reporter witnesses a murder and is unable to persuade anyone to believe the story. Critics also pointed to similar themes—voyeurism, sexual guilt, violence with Freudian overtones—and similar techniques such as involving the audience with a character and then killing him off, using humor to release tension, and a flashy camera style. De Palma even enticed Hitchcock's longtime composer Bernard Herrmann out of retirement to write the score for this film.

He admits that *Sisters* was "obviously influenced by Hitchcock," but insists that "it had a life of its own." Hitchcock, he has said, "is a textbook of film grammar and counterpoint. He's used every kind of visual connection in cinema, yet he's impossible to imitate." De Palma sees his own films as "much more romantic" than Hitchcock's. "I kind of temper my imagery with romantic music, emotionality, and slow motion."

With his next film, *Phantom of the Paradise*, De Palma moved deeper into his chosen genre. The Paradise is a rock palace. It is haunted by a composer whose music was stolen by an evil entrepreneur who has made a pact with the devil. De Palma chose this setting because "the rock world is so stylized and expressionistic to begin with, that it would be a perfect environment in which to tell old horror tales." He had observed the increasing use of horror and violence in acts like the Rolling Stones and Alice Cooper, and wanted to show what that said about contemporary culture.

The violence in this film—when, for instance, the composer's face is crushed in a record presser—drew criticism, as did the bloody murder in *Sisters* and scenes in all his later films. De Palma has answered that "because of my very sort of formalistic training, I sometimes go for what is the strongest, most vivid color on the palette, which in the case of movies is violence."

For *Obsession*, De Palma again used Bernard Herrmann's music. And the story is very close to that of Hitchcock's film *Vertigo*. A man (Cliff Robertson) obsessed with his wife (Genevieve Bujold), who was kidnapped and killed, believes he finds her again in another woman, who turns out to be his daughter. The complex plot is a plan by the man's evil business partner to take over both shares of their real-estate company. Some critics saw the film as a poor copy, but De Palma said that it was another filmmaking assignment he had given himself; he wanted to try to create an intense romantic relationship between two characters.

His next film was a professional turning point for De Palma. Though *Carrie*'s budget was still small (less than $2 million), it was the first film since *Rabbit* that he'd made for a major studio (United Artists); it received good reviews from respectable critics; and two of the actors—Sissy Spacek (Carrie) and Piper Laurie (her mother in the film) were nominated for Academy Awards.

The script was adapted from a novel about a young girl who has telekinetic power—the ability to move objects with her mind. Carrie is being raised by her puritanical, religiously fanatic mother and is an outcast in her high school.

A sympathetic classmate, Sue Snell (Amy Irving), arranges a date for Carrie for the senior prom with handsome, blond Tommy Ross, her own boyfriend. Unknown to her, Chris (Nancy Allen), another classmate, plans a nasty trick to ruin this dream for Carrie. She and her boyfriend (John Travolta) rig the election so that Carrie is voted queen of the prom. Then, when she is standing on the stage wearing her crown, they release a bucket of pig's blood on her from above.

In her fury, Carrie uses her telekinetic power to wreak vengeful destruction all around her—tables overturn, hoses unfurl and blast streams of water, bodies fly. Finally, as she walks out, the room is consumed by fire.

Carrie returns to a house lit by hundreds of candles. Her mothers stands ready with a knife to kill her witch daughter. Instead, Carrie galvanizes all the blades in the house to crucify her mother against a wall and then shuts herself in a closet as the house goes up in flames.

The religious imagery in the film came easily to De Palma. Although he and his brothers were raised as Protestants and went to Quaker schools, the Catholic atmosphere of his father's

Italian-American family "made an indelible impression." Memories from family weddings and funerals—"all those grandparents hovering about and all those candles!"—provided him with "mysterious or terrifying images."

De Palma saw *Carrie* as a culmination of his development so far: "I sort of put everything in *Carrie*," he has said. "I had the romantic story between Tommy Ross and Carrie White; I had all the visual suspense elements; and I was using everything I knew, including comedy and improvisation, from all the other pictures I had made." He also used difficult camera and editing techniques. It took him weeks and weeks to cut the prom scene because he had extended the suspense with slow motion. He spent more weeks cutting the destruction scene into split screen, with Carrie on one side and the flying objects on the other. Otherwise he would have had to cut back and forth between the two again and again. (In reviewing the film for himself later, he was dissatisfied with the effect and concluded that the split screen was a distraction here.)

He was satisfied, however, with the audience's response to the surprise ending. In a dream, Sue goes to the spot where Carrie is buried. As she lays down her flowers, a bloody hand suddenly springs from the earth to grab her. "Never have I seen an audience so universally affected. . . . It gives you real sense of satisfaction when you've emotionally caught up your audience. It's something I've never quite been able to do before."

Carrie was also a major turning point, personally, for the shy, introverted boy who had grown up to be called "the coldest hot director in town." He had told an interviewer in 1973, "I'm almost completely oblivious to my surroundings. I have no desire to own anything. I've never married and don't want to marry. The outside world means little or nothing to me. I'm completely obsessed with film. Everything meaningful is right here in my head, behind my eyes."

There was, in fact, no one woman in his life. He had dated

Margot Kidder when she was starring in *Sisters* and was reported to have had an "intense" relationship with Genevieve Bujold (*Obsession*). But it was a young actress who failed to get the part of Carrie who changed his mind.

De Palma cast Nancy Allen as Chris, Carrie's chief tormentor, because he likes to cast against type, and the contrast between the character's mean nature and Allen's sweet appearance appealed to him. During the filming she thought he didn't like her because he was never particularly friendly. But that is just his style, which he describes as being "very professional." He explained: "I come to the set and am very detached. I'm very much involved in making sure the cinematic design is correct, and I'm trying to think of new ideas. I don't sit there and chat it up with everybody, or pat people on the back."

Nevertheless, she took him up three months later on an open invitation to the cast to visit the studio and watch one of their scenes being edited. That visit turned into a three-year long-distance romance (he was in New York; she was in Los Angeles). Then, on January 12, 1979, they invited fifteen friends over for a party. De Palma assigned a student to film the guests' reactions as they learned that it was a surprise wedding reception.

Allen describes her husband as "very loving and warm" and "*not* a very weird person." They live a quiet life (which they have said will someday include children) in a brownstone in Greenwich Village. Since their marriage, Allen has appeared in all of De Palma's films. In 1980, after *Home Movies*, they separated for a while. "It was just too much togetherness," she said. But after three months, they were back together again, personally and professionally.

After *Carrie*, De Palma was naturally sent piles of similar scripts. He chose to make *The Fury*, which is about two telekinetic teenagers kidnapped by mysterious scientists for use as secret weapons. The story is based on the search of the father of one of them (played by Kirk Douglas) for his son. The film begins and ends with killings.

De Palma thought at the time that he was doing the film for sound reasons. The script had the potential of being visually interesting. "When you're dealing with the interior of someone's mind," he has said, "you can do all sorts of stylized things." And he was given enough time and money ($6.5 million, his biggest budget) to come up with "elaborate cinematic ideas." He was also still teaching himself the art of filmmaking, and he wanted the challenge of making an action picture.

Now he sees *The Fury* as a mistake, and in part he blames his old enemy, Hollywood: "In this business success can be even more destructive than failure, because it can isolate you and leave you surrounded by film people talking about deals and budgets and percentage points, and so you yourself begin to forget what you want to do. Because you have some big star and a terrific deal, you forget to worry about whether this is a movie you should really make."

Although the film was popular at the box office, many reviewers found the story silly and confused and felt that De Palma had used camera tricks for their own sake. He denied that charge and explained, as an example, why he used slow motion for the killing of Hester, a sympathetic character. He wanted to increase the drama and also to convey her point of view: "She's happy and exhilarated and then *pow!* the car hits her." His own evaluation was: "The story and script were way too complicated, and a complicated style such as mine on top of that made it impossible to follow."

In 1978, just as De Palma was getting a firm foothold in Hollywood, he decided to leave commercial filmmaking to teach a course in feature production to fifteen students at Sarah Lawrence College. He taught them how to make a low-budget movie from start to finish: "I wanted to prove that it still can be done." He said that he was considered an aberration in the business, because "a hot director simply doesn't take off two years to do such a thing." But for him it was a relief. He has said, "I was, in a way, going back to my roots, working the way I used to work when I was their age—and at the same time escaping from all those industry types who can turn you inside out."

The film he made with his students is called *Home Movies*. It is a farce about a serious teenage boy who takes home movies of his family. De Palma has described it as "the mad story of a lunatic family" and has also claimed that it is about his own family. It took twice as long to make as a normal feature would have because De Palma had to explain how to do everything—from writing the script to getting financing ($350,000).

Although the list of investors besides De Palma included Steven Spielberg, George Lucas, and Kirk Douglas (who played a role in *Home Movies*), the filmmakers were unable to get a major distributor. Instead, UA Classics, a division of United Artists for films with specialized appeal, distributed it. De Palma complained that the reason the film did poorly was that UA did not spend enough money on promotion, and he even put up some of his own.

De Palma's next two films were commercial movies with large budgets: *Dressed to Kill* cost $7.5 million and *Blow Out* cost $18 million. He wrote both scripts himself, and Nancy Allen played leading roles. She was a high-class call girl in the first film and a small-time prostitute in the second.

Dressed to Kill is about the murder of a middle-aged woman (played by Angie Dickinson), after she is picked up by a man in a museum, and the tracking down of the murderer by her teenage son—an electronics whiz—and a call girl who found the body. De Palma has said of it, "I let my subconscious fears swim to the surface"—fears of what can happen besides sex when you get picked up; of being alone on a subway platform, in an elevator, in your own bathroom.

He has also said, "To me, *Dressed to Kill* is a distillation of all the suspense forms. . . . This story is the most structured of all those I've done. . . . It's a pure study in style—nothing but style. There's almost no dialogue. It's not so much a departure as an

evolving of my form and style. The form is the content." The
only sound in the long museum pickup scene, for instance, is
that of footfalls on the hard floor.

The film got ecstatic reviews from many major critics, although it also elicited criticisms familiar by now to De Palma.
Andrew Sarris in the *Village Voice* called it a "shamefully straight
steal from *Psycho*, among other things." De Palma uses the famous shower scene and also the psychiatrist explaining the killer's
psychosis—in this case, a moralistic transvestite (Michael Caine)
punishing promiscuous women.

Some critics objected to the violence in the film. Blood pours
through shower curtains and an elevator, and, in fact, De Palma
had to re-edit and cut in order to get an R rating rather than an X.
Others saw such devices as the split screens, super slow motion,
jump cuts, overhead crane shots, and a screen within the screen
as style for its own sake.

For his next film, De Palma chose to do a character study.
Looking for a new challenge, he decided to try to correct what he
saw as his weakness as a director. "I'm usually so involved in the
visual storytelling," he has said, "that the slow rising and falling of
the character's relationships just don't interest me." This is evident in the fact that his rough cuts, unlike those of most directors,
are usually shorter than the final version. "I throw all the character scenes out," he once said. "The film runs like a crazy windup
toy. Then I start building them back in again."

He got the idea for *Blow Out* after he did *Carrie*. His sound-
effects man on that film went on vacation, and De Palma noticed
that he took his tape recorder along. "I began to wonder what sort
of man chooses that profession," he said. In *Blow Out*, Jack (John
Travolta), the sound-effects man for a film company that makes
sexy thrillers, is innocently collecting sounds (an owl, the wind)
one night when he hears a tire blow out and sees a car crash into
the water. He rescues a young woman from the car, but the man
with her (a candidate for President) is dead. Listening to his tape

later, he realizes that the blowout was actually a gunshot, and he determines to solve the dangerous mystery.

The film was criticized for putting too much emphasis on style and not enough on logic. But in the *New Yorker*, Pauline Kael, a devout De Palma fan, called it "a great movie." In her review, she wrote, "For the first time, De Palma goes inside his central character . . . and stays inside . . . *Blow Out* is the first movie in which De Palma has stripped away the cackle and the glee. . . . He's playing it straight, and asking you—trusting you—to respond." She also wrote, "This is the first film he has made about the things that really matter to him."

One of these things is his pessimistic political vision. "I have this real sense of the effects of the capitalistic society in which everything is done for the sake of profit," he said recently. "It's totally attacked the moral fiber, and I'm very interested in how it affects the lives of people who go up against it—*Blow Out* is very much about that. I don't think the system can be changed. It's too strong and powerful—it just engulfs you."

George Lucas on location with *Raiders of the Lost Ark*. PHOTO: Courtesy of Lucasfilm, Ltd.

George Lucas

THX–1138 (1971)
American Graffiti (1973)
Star Wars (1977)
The Empire Strikes Back (1980, executive producer)
Raiders of the Lost Ark (1981, executive producer)
Return of the Jedi (1983, executive producer)

GEORGE LUCAS doesn't look like a prodigy. He is a short, almost painfully shy young man, who usually dresses in jeans and sneakers and hides behind glasses and a bushy black beard. Yet the film critic Stephen Farber wrote that "at twenty-eight" Lucas was "already one of the world's master directors." At thirty-six, according to *Fortune* magazine, he was "the most successful executive in the beleaguered motion-picture business." What is prodigious about George Lucas is his ability to change the ordinary stuff of his own childhood into movies that capture the imagination of millions of children and adults.

What was the stuff of that childhood? George Lucas was born in the rural town of Modesto, California, on May 14, 1944. He has described his family as "middle middle class." His father owned a stationery and office supply store and farmed in his spare time. George and his three sisters were raised on a walnut ranch just outside town.

83

Lucas didn't grow up as a movie fan. There were few theaters in Modesto and when he went to the movies, he has said, "I really didn't pay much attention. I was usually going to look for girls and goof off." Instead he listened to rock 'n' roll, watched Flash Gordon and the Republic adventure serials on television, and hung around his father's store reading the comic books on the racks. He still listens to rock 'n' roll and has a giant collection of 78 rpms from the fifties and sixties. He also continues to read science fiction and now collects both books and art works in that area.

As a teenager, Lucas has said, "I was a hell-raiser." He "lived, ate, breathed cars! That was everything for me." With his small, souped-up Fiat, he drove around Modesto like the teenagers in *American Graffiti*. He got a job rebuilding cars at a foreign-car garage and worked on pit crews at races around the country. He even won some trophies and dreamed of being a racing car driver.

Then two days before he was to graduate from high school (with a "D-plus, plus average"), Lucas's car was hit by a driver going ninety miles an hour. He was thrown clear and broke only two bones, but his lungs were crushed, and he spent three months in the hospital. "Before the accident," he has said, "I never used to think. Afterward, I realized I had to plan if I was ever to be happy."

His first decision was to become a serious student. He enrolled as a social science major at Modesto Junior College, and he began to paint. When he graduated, he wanted to go to art school, but his father was afraid he would become a beatnik and refused to pay his tuition. Lucas was working at the time as a mechanic on a racing car for Haskell Wexler, the famous cinematographer. Lucas had taken still pictures for car racers and played around with a friend's 8-millimeter camera, but he "didn't really know what films were all about." Nevertheless, Wexler whetted his interest and helped him get into the University of

Southern California film school, which his father considered respectable.

He planned to study still photography and animation. Instead, he discovered Fellini, Truffaut, Godard, and the underground filmmakers of San Francisco. "Movies replaced my love for cars. . . . When I finally discovered film, I really fell madly in love with it, ate it and slept it twenty-four hours a day."

Lucas was a star student at USC, sweeping the awards at film festivals. He made eight movies while he was in school because he was willing to break rules, like buying extra footage for what were supposed to be class projects. He believes that "nobody's *ever* going to let anybody make a movie. You have to go out and do it!"

This, he has said, is his philosophy of life and "one of the main thrusts in all the films . . . the fact that if you apply yourself and work real hard, you can get what you want accomplished. Your only limitations are your own willingness to do whatever you want to do. In *THX* . . . the whole film, really, is the analogy that we're in cages and the doors are open. We just don't want to leave . . . . *American Graffiti*'s saying the same thing . . . that you have to go out into the world and make something of yourself—no matter how frightening that is. And it recurs in *Star Wars* with Luke wanting something, but not wanting it enough to break the rules and say, 'Okay, I'm going to do it.'" In *The Empire Strikes Back* and *Return of the Jedi* (the third movie in the series), "It's the same thing but more inward than outward. More personal."

Lucas's first films were "very abstract—tone poems, visual. . . . I didn't want to know about stories and plot and characters." One, *The Emperor*, is a documentary about a disc jockey, a subject he returned to in *American Graffiti*. *THX–1138*, an award-winning exercise in lighting, was the basis of his first feature.

In film school, editing had been Lucas's first love, and he still says it's "what I can really sit and do and lose track of time and enjoy myself." (His former wife Marcia is a well-respected film editor, who has worked on his films as well as those of Scorsese and others.) But the jobs he got after graduation as a grip, cameraman, assistant editor, and editor convinced him that he wanted to direct. "I really didn't like people telling me how to do this and how to do that . . . carrying out someone else's ideas that I really didn't think were so great."

Lucas won a scholarship from Warner Brothers to watch the shooting of *Finian's Rainbow*. On a similar scholarship, he had watched Carl Foreman direct *McKenna's Gold*, a conventional Hollywood film. Lucas made an award-winning behind-the-scenes film, supposedly about that experience, but really more about the desert where the film took place than about the film itself. He had been bored watching Foreman and wasn't eager to do something like that again. But this time it would be different. The director of *Finian's Rainbow* was Francis Coppola, who would become for Lucas both friend and mentor.

Lucas ended up staying with Coppola as a "general do-everything" for his next film, *The Rain People*. The forty-minute documentary he made about it, called *Filmmaker*, is considered one of the best films on filmmaking. He then became a vice-president of Coppola's production company, Zoetrope, and in his own words was Coppola's "right hand for ten years." Yet, according to Lucas, no two people could be more different. "Francis spends every day jumping off a cliff and hoping he's going to land okay. My main interest is security. . . . But the goals we have in mind are the same. We want to make movies and be free from the yoke of the studios."

Lucas has said that he learned "the way I make movies" from Coppola. It was Coppola who forced him to become a writer, though he was never good in English in school and had done terribly in scriptwriting classes. Even now, he finds writing an "agonizing" experience.

But Coppola insisted that he add a plot to *THX* so that American Zoetrope could produce it as a feature. It took four drafts and several collaborations to create the story of a man in a dehumanized, drug-oriented, future world, who tries to escape. Robert Duvall, his head shaved, played the lead.

Coppola produced *THX* for Warner Brothers on a tiny budget, which allowed the director only $15,000. The slick-looking film was shot entirely on location. The crew and all the equipment traveled in a van to the twenty-two unlikely filming sites—the unfinished tunnels of the San Francisco subway system, for instance, where a jet car and jet motorcycle chase took place.

The Warners executives who saw the rough cut hated it, and Lucas blames them for the lack of publicity the film got. But he was angrier still that they cut a few minutes without his approval.

THX got mixed reviews but brought George Lucas a cult following. It was chosen for an award by a radical directors' group at the Cannes Film Festival. When Warners refused to pay their fare, Lucas and his wife packed their backpacks and spent their last $2,000 to get there.

George Lucas's second film, *American Graffiti*, seems completely different from his first. "*THX* is very much the way that I am as a filmmaker," he has said. "*American Graffiti* is very much the way I am as a person." *THX* earned Lucas a reputation as a very cold science fiction director, and he wasn't being offered any scripts. Coppola told him he had to prove that he could write something warm and human. What he came up with was a script for a "rock 'n' roll cruising movie." He wrote it himself ("kicking and screaming"), but he asked two friends from film school to rewrite it. "The scenes are mine," he has said. "The dialogue is theirs."

Lucas spent a year and a half trying to sell *American Graffiti*

to a studio. Universal Studios finally took it on the condition
that Coppola agree to be the coproducer. Lucas was given a budget
of about $700,000. Of that, his fee was $20,000 and he spent
$80,000 on forty-two rock songs that made up the sound track.
The opening shot is a closeup of the markings on a radio dial and
the background is a steady stream of fifties radio music with
fragments from a disc jockey's (Wolfman Jack's) monologue.

The film interweaves the stories of four young men on the eve
of their graduation from a small-town high school in Northern
California in 1962 (the same year Lucas graduated). They are all
at turning points, which are played out during the twelve hours
between dusk and daylight, mainly in their ever-cruising cars and
at Mel's Burger City Drive-In.

Two of them—Steve and Curt—are supposed to leave the next
morning for college in the East. Steve is class president, freckle-
faced and all-American. His cheerleader girl friend doesn't want
him to go. Curt, the class intellectual, is picked up by a gang of
hoods and forced to carry out their demands. Once he has proved
himself, he decides to search out the real Wolfman Jack. Terry,
with his buckteeth and freckles, is an outsider, who never can
quite keep up with the others because he doesn't have a car.
Tonight he borrows one and gets a girl. Finally, John Milner is
the future. Five years older than the others, he is still cruising in
his "piss-yellow deuce coupe." He wins the climactic drag race
but realizes that he is over the hill.

Having learned from Coppola the importance of actors, Lucas
spent four months casting *American Graffiti*. For twelve to fourteen hours a day, six days a week, he interviewed everyone, giving
them five or ten minutes apiece. "I like to get someone who I feel
more or less *is* the character," he has said, "and then utilize his
own personal capacity and personality traits." He worked the
same way on *Star Wars*, a film that took three months to cast.

Yet, the actual directing of actors seems to make him slightly
uncomfortable. Richard Dreyfuss, who played Curt, joked that it

was three weeks before he knew that his director spoke English. According to Coppola, Lucas leads his actors indirectly: "He constructs his scenes so specifically, or narrowly . . . that everything comes out more or less the way he sees it." Lucas himself believes that he has an advantage as a director because "I know exactly what I want. . . . Life becomes for me whatever it is that I'm making a movie about for the year or two that I'm making it. So, when the time comes for me to tell an actor to do this or that, there is no question in my mind what he should do."

Lucas found directing *American Graffiti* a "rather horrendous experience." Since the film takes place at night, it had to be shot at night—twenty-eight nights, shooting from 9:00 P.M. to 5:00 A.M. At first Lucas tried to be both director and cinematographer, as he had been on *THX*, but he couldn't do it. He hired two cameramen and then called in his old friend Haskell Wexler to help him get the look he wanted—"all yellow and red and orange . . . very much like a carnival."

The studio executives again hated his film. They wanted to sell it as a TV movie; they wanted to change the title to *Another Slow Night in Modesto*. According to Lucas, half of them didn't know what *American Graffiti* meant; they thought it sounded like an Italian movie or a movie about feet. They did release it finally, but in a form that violated Lucas's vision: they cut about five minutes and did not use the stereophonic sound that was designed for it. (When Lucas re-released the film in 1978, he corrected both of these defects.)

To Universal's surprise, the film became the studio's biggest hit of all time and one of the most popular films of the 1970s. It was nominated for five Academy Awards, and the screenplay won awards from the New York Film Critics Circle and the National Society of Film Critics.

Almost all reviewers praised the technical achievements of *American Graffiti*—the cinematography, editing, and acting. But they divided over whether it is a serious film or just superficial nostalgia. Lucas has said that it is not about the sixties, but about change, "about teenagers accepting the fact that they have to leave home. It's about the end of an era, how things can't stay the same." As one boy in the film says to another, "You can't stay seventeen forever."

Lucas does acknowledge the film's autobiographical roots. "It all happened to me, but I sort of glamorized it. I spent four years of my life cruising the main street of my home town. . . . I started as Terry the toad, but then I went on to be John Milner, the local drag race champion, and then I became Curt Henderson, the intellectual who goes off to college. They were all composite characters, based on my life, and on the lives of friends of mine."

Success didn't change George Lucas's life. With typical generosity, he gave part of the profits from the film to the main actors and continued to live frugally on his wife's salary as an editor. He invested most of the money he got in his next project, a "space fantasy" for children called *Star Wars*. He had had the idea in mind before he started shooting *American Graffiti*, and he began researching and writing it as soon as the film was done.

Lucas had two reasons for wanting to make this film. As a director, he wanted the challenge of making a real movie, one with plot and characters that would require the use of sound stages with sets, "the way they used to make movies." As a filmmaker, he wanted to create a modern fairy tale. "As a student of anthropology," he has said, "I feel strongly about the role myths and fairy tales play in setting up young people for the way they're supposed to handle themselves in society." He thinks that "young people don't have a fantasy life anymore, not the way *we* did. All they've got is Kojak and Dirty Harry. There're all these kids running around, wanting to be killer cops."

While he was writing, Lucas read books on mythology, fantasy, and anthropology. This he combined with the "flotsam and jetsam from the period when I was twelve years old. All the books and films and comics that I liked when I was a child."

After two and a half years of full-time work, he had written four different versions of the script. The first version, which he rejected, centered completely on the robots. The final version consisted of six films in two trilogies. (He added a third after the success of *Star Wars* and has said that the full cycle should take about twenty years to film.) Although humans now have the central roles, only the robots R2-D2 and C-3PO appear in all the episodes. "In effect, the story will be told through their eyes," Lucas has said.

He chose to begin with episode four of *Star Wars*, *The New Hope*, because it has the most action. There are lightsaber fights between Luke Skywalker and Darth Vader and spaceship chases and battles, all set against a war between the Imperial and Rebel forces "in a galaxy far away."

Lucas showed his script to almost every major studio before 20th Century-Fox was willing to take a chance on it and agree to his demand for control over final cut, merchandising, and publicity. He was given a budget of $8.5 million (he eventually spent $9.5 million) and a cast and crew of 950, compared with the forty he had had before. Yet he considers *Star Wars* a "real low-budget movie."

He had had to pare down his original budget estimate of $18 million, and, as a result, the film is full of compromises. He cut out over a hundred special-effects shots. New sets were made from old sets. Space weapons were made out of cut-down machine guns. The robots didn't work right at first. The original R2-D2 couldn't go more than three feet without running into something. (Extra footage was shot later with a rebuilt robot for some movie shots to be used at the beginning.) Even the cantina scene, in which Luke (Mark Hamill) and Ben Kenobi (Alec Guinness) hire Han Solo (Harrison Ford) and Chewbacca from among a roomful of bizarre, otherworldly creatures, is only a shadow of what was in Lucas's imagination. The designer fell sick, and the studio wouldn't give Lucas enough money to have someone fully complete it. "The film is about 25 percent of what I wanted it to be," he has said.

Lucas formed his own company, Industrial Light and Magic, to supply *Star Wars* with its 365 special-effects shots. These shots, some of which combined from five to thirty elements, required models, computers, special cameras, mattes, and blue screens. They took up almost half the budget and were visible for half the running time of the film. ILM also created every sound in *Star Wars*, since a door slamming or a foot falling on the planet Tatooine couldn't be the same as that sound on earth. An ordinary film has two hundred sound units; *Star Wars* has two thousand.

The special-effects company would be used for Lucas's future films. One-fifth of *The Empire Strikes Back* was shot by ILM without actors, as were some of the escapes and supernatural aspects of *Raiders of the Lost Ark*, and most of the 942 special effects in *Return of the Jedi*. ILM is now a big, expensively equipped company that does work for other filmmakers as well and is noted for its glossy professionalism.

The team Lucas hired for ILM was relatively young and inexperienced. He knew exactly the effects he wanted for *Star Wars*, and he was looking for people who would produce them without question. Then he worked very closely with them, spending months with the artists who sculpted C-3PO's face and the technicians who developed R2-D2's vocabulary of beeps, whistles, sighs, and eeks. He described C-3PO as "an overly emotional, fussy robot." He didn't want his face to be inhuman; he wanted it to be one people could respond to.

The whole film was meticulously drawn out in advance on storyboards. Lucas also put together World War II and Korean

War movie footage to show how he wanted the air fights between the spaceships to look.

With *Star Wars*, as with his earlier films, Lucas could not delegate responsibility. "If I left anything for a day, it would fall apart, and it's purely because I set it up that way," he has said. By the end of the filming, he was exhausted and depressed. He was also permanently soured on directing. "I spent all my time yelling and screaming at people, and I have never had to do that before." He has also said, "I've discovered what I knew all along: I am not a film director. I'm a filmmaker. A film director is somebody who directs people—large operations. I like to sit down behind a camera and shoot pretty pictures and then cut them together and watch the magic come as I combine images and tell stories."

Lucas expected the movie to be "moderately successful," and he flew off to Hawaii with his wife for a vacation before he could find out whether or not it was doing well. In fact, *Star Wars* was the most lucrative movie up to that time, grossing about $500 million. Lucas got between $22 and $26 million for himself ($12 million after taxes). It could have been more, but he gave away one-quarter of his profits to the actors, people on the set, and his office employees. As for himself and his wife (the couple Francis Coppola once called "country mice"), he has said, "On a personal level it doesn't mean much of a change. . . . Once you have a car and a house there's not much more you can do except eat out more."

Star Wars opened to almost unanimous praise from reviewers of widely different tastes and ages and won seven Academy Awards. Reviewers called it "magnificent," "grand," "glorious," and "exhilarating," even while admitting that it was pure escapism.

After *Star Wars*, George Lucas stated his intent never to direct again. "Now I can go back to what I want to do," he has said, "experimental, abstract kinds of things, working with pure form."

His plan was to support this by supervising sequels to *American Graffiti* and *Star Wars*.

True to his word, in part at least, he became a producer and chairman of the board of Lucasfilm Limited. In 1981, he closed the doors on directing and resigned from the Directors Guild of America, the Writers Guild of America, and the Academy of Motion Picture Arts and Sciences. These resignations came in the wake of a $250,000 fine for putting Irvin Kershner's credit at the end rather than the beginning of *The Empire Strikes Back*, even though the director had consented to the end credit.

As a producer, Lucas has said, "I might have more decisions to make, but the pressures seem less enormous." His first production was *More American Graffiti*. He developed the story but was not directly involved in the production, and it was a critical and box office failure, Lucas's only one. Then Lucas used almost all of his earnings from *Star Wars* as collateral to borrow the $22 million he needed to produce episode five of *Star Wars*, *The Empire Strikes Back* (the film ended up costing $30 million). Since he was financing it, he could keep all the profits after the costs of distribution.

The Empire Strikes Back grossed about $350 million, but the critical consensus was that it is not as much fun as the original *Star Wars*. It is difficult to separate Lucas's contributions to the film from those of the director, Irvin Kershner. At one time Lucas said, "It's truly Kershner's movie." At another, he said, "I'm the boss." In fact, Lucas wrote the story (though not the script), created the storyboards, was sent black-and-white videotapes daily, gave technical advice, oversaw the editing and special effects, and spent six weeks polishing the sound and images in a sound-mixing room. Kershner himself admits to working in Lucas's mold: "I was trying to keep the convention that George Lucas set up where you stay with no scene very long. . . and where the editorial rhythm is in a way more important than the camera moves or the actors saying their lines."

Steven Spielberg played a similar role as director of Lucas's next project, *Raiders of the Lost Ark*. "The movie stylistically is very loyal to George's concept and impulse," he said. "It's as if I slipped into George's shoes and directed the picture as George might have . . . rather than imposing my style onto the project." He also said he learned creative shortcuts from Lucas—"how to give the audience the eyeful with *illusions* of grandeur." Lucas collaborated on the script for this film, helped with the special effects, did the editing, and at Spielberg's invitation also went on location.

Raiders won praise as escapist entertainment. It is a sophisticated adventure movie about an archaeologist-adventurer named Indiana Jones (Harrison Ford), who is in pursuit of a supernatural treasure, the lost Ark of the Covenant. It is based on a story Lucas wrote ten years earlier, and he has already mapped out story lines for four planned sequels. One of these, *Indiana Jones: The Temple of Doom*, is in production. "What interests me here," Lucas has said, "is this fascinating character. If I could be a dream figure, I'd be Indy. It's not just that I'm interested in archeology or anthropology. . . . It's that Indy can do *anything*. . . . He's this renegade archeologist and adventurer, but he's also a college professor, and he's got his Cary Grant side."

Lucas was again a looming presence on the set of the next *Star Wars* episode, *Return of the Jedi*. Although he chose another director (Richard Marquand), he wrote the first draft of the script and he has said, "I want these three films to have a unity because it's one story. I knew I had to be here to keep the look of it consistent, the art direction consistent, the technology consistent."

But George Lucas is also a businessman and has to spend time making deals as well as films. "Business is a necessary evil for me now," he said in late 1980. "I'm trying to turn the studio system around. The studios use films they don't have the vaguest idea how to make to earn profits for their shareholders. I'm using my profits to make films." Lucasfilm Limited is a multimillion-dollar entertainment company that concentrates on filmmaking and related merchandising activities, such as selling the dolls, games, and T-shirts made by the fifty or sixty licensees of *Star Wars* and *The Empire Strikes Back*, whose gross retail sales so far have been about $1.5 billion. Lucasfilm employs about 350 people, owns Industrial Light and Magic, and has extensive post-production facilities.

Lucas runs the company tightly but definitely in his own style. Many of the top executives are film school graduates or are at least very knowledgeable about film. His employees work hard but are paid well. He refuses to license his films for use on liquor or cigarettes or toys with sharp edges, and because he himself is a diabetic, he asked the licensee for *Star Wars* chewing gum to offer a sugarless variety.

He also has a vision of a community of filmmakers living and working together. This vision should take form by 1984 on what he calls Skywalker Ranch, a 3,000-acre $20 million enclosure in the Marin County Hills, where all of Lucasfilm except ILM will be moved. Lucas himself designed the main building in a Victorian style, like his own home in a San Francisco suburb. "Writers need privacy," he has said, "and Victorian houses are full of cubbyholes." He has described Skywalker Ranch as "a creative retreat where filmmakers can meet, study, collaborate, write, edit, and experiment with new filmmaking ideas."

George Lucas is a controversial figure right now. He keeps talking about the experimental films that he wants to make—as soon as the ranch is ready. "My ambition," he has said, "is to make movies, but all by myself, to shoot them, cut them, make stuff I want to, just for my own exploration, to see if I can combine images in a certain way. My movies will go back to the way my first films were, which dealt a little more realistically with the human condition." But some critics don't believe him. Stuart Byron, in the *Village Voice*, called him "the most reactionary filmmaker in America," and Pauline Kael, in the *New Yorker*, accused him of being in the toy business and wrote that he is "hooked on the crap of his childhood."

When *Jedi* opened in May 1983, Lucas announced that he was taking a two-year sabbatical from Lucasfilm. A month later he announced the break-up of his thirteen-year marriage. During the sabbatical he plans to read and write, and also to spend time with his two-year-old adopted daughter, for whom he will share custody. Maybe at the end of that time, one side of his genius will have prevailed—the filmmaker side or the toymaker side.

Paul Mazursky

Paul Mazursky

Bob and Carol and Ted and Alice (1969)
Alex in Wonderland (1970)
Blume in Love (1973)
Harry and Tonto (1974)
Next Stop, Greenwich Village (1976)
An Unmarried Woman (1978)
Willie and Phil (1980)
Tempest (1982)

"IN MY TIME," Paul Mazursky has recalled, "we all wanted to be in the theater; movies were a kind of sell-out. I never fantasized that I wanted to direct films." What he did fantasize about was a career as an actor—something he hasn't entirely abandoned. Since he began directing, Mazursky has given himself cameo roles in several of his films and has appeared in two films by other directors—A Star Is Born and A Man, a Woman, and a Bank. And he has always received good notices.

Paul Mazursky was born Irwin Mazursky in Brownsville, a lower-middle-class Jewish section of Brooklyn, on April 25, 1930. During the depression his father worked as a ditch digger. Later he got a job loading trucks. Mazursky has described his mother as a "very powerful woman with tremendous energy that was not used, not plugged in. So it frizzed all over the joint." (Not unlike the mother in Next Stop, Greenwich Village.)

It was his grandfather, however, his mother's father, who introduced him to literature and culture. A Russian émigré who ran a candy store down the block, he would play the violin for his grandson and talk about the great Russian writers, whom he had reread in English.

Mazursky's dream of being an actor began in childhood. From the age of twelve, he read every play he could find. He had roles in high-school plays and continued acting at Brooklyn College, where he was a speech therapy and English literature major. During his senior year he starred in an Off-Broadway production and changed his name to Paul. ("I hated the name Irwin from the day I way born. To me, a schnook.")

Then he got his big break—a leading role in *Fear and Desire*, a film about a soldier who goes berserk and the first feature made by the now famous director Stanley Kubrick. "I thought it was the big time. I was paid a hundred dollars a week for a month's work and had a free round trip to California. And I had my Academy Award speech all written out, in which I thanked the dean for giving me a leave of absence to do the picture." But *Fear and Desire* was a flop, and reviewers criticized Mazursky for overacting.

Nevertheless, it made his fantasy of being an actor real; he felt like a professional. After graduation, he moved to Greenwich Village, studied acting with Paul Mann and Lee Strasberg, and waited for another break. It came in 1954, when he was cast as a juvenile delinquent in *The Blackboard Jungle*, a big commercial film.

But his acting career never took hold. About the next five years, he has said, "I almost never had an acting job that lasted as much as three weeks." He spent the rest of his time as a bit actor on television, a nightclub comic, an acting teacher, the director of a unsuccessful Off-Broadway revue, an unpublished short story writer, and a sales clerk in a health food store.

In the late 1950s, Larry Tucker, owner of a club in which

Mazursky had performed, asked him to help start an improvisational comic revue in Los Angeles. Since live TV had dried up by this time in New York, Mazursky agreed. He packed up and left, with his wife and one-year-old daughter.

While he was working with Tucker on this and other revues, Mazursky was also acting and writing on his own. He wrote his own nightclub routines and started writing television scripts, though he was unable to sell any of them. He also wrote a twelve-minute film, *Last Year at Malibu*. It was a parody of the arty New Wave directors, and he dubbed the narration in phony French, Swedish, and Japanese.

In 1963 Mazursky and Tucker were both hired as writers for "The Danny Kaye Show" on TV, where they worked for four years. Although he was making $75,000 a year, Mazursky was unhappy. He continued to act occasionally with a repertory company and, always a film buff, took courses in cutting and editing. He has said of that time, "I knew I wasn't going to try to be an actor anymore or make a living as a comedy writer. I was going to direct films or get out of show business."

During the summers he and Tucker worked toward that goal. First they wrote a screenplay titled *H–Bomb Beach Party*. which was sold but never filmed. Then they wrote *I Love You, Alice B. Toklas*, a comic satire about the romance between a lawyer in his forties and a hippie. It was sold and made into a successful film starring Peter Sellers. This gave them the bargaining power they needed when they peddled their next script, *Bob and Carol and Ted and Alice*. Mazursky could demand—and get—the right to direct and the chance to begin his career as a filmmaker.

All of Mazursky's films have a common theme. He calls them "inner journeys" and "painful comedies." They are satires, but they are gentle, because of his attitude toward his characters and toward life. He writes about what he knows—typically the affluent middle-class America of white, liberal professionals— and he feels compassion for his characters—"because I'm one of them," he explained. "I'm always writing about real people in specific situations," he has said. "The humor in my films comes out of those real situations."

Mazursky takes love seriously, he believes in marriage, and he is basically optimistic. All his films end, he has said, "with the feeling of affirmation—or at least the feeling of the *possibility* of affirmation."

He usually keeps the look of his films simple. The most striking visual element is likely to be the expression on an actor's face. "If the audience is aware of the camera's movement," he has said, "it takes away from the story."

Mazursky's films seem improvisational, although they usually stay very close to the script. "Generally I don't like to shoot improvisation," he has said. "Actors can get hooked on a lot of things that seem like fun at the time but have nothing to do with what I wrote. I want to respect myself as a writer." He does, however, occasionally add nonprofessionals to the cast (like the psychiatrists in several of his films) to give a documentary flavor.

The most consistent criticism of Mazursky's movies is the charge of sentimentality. "I've always defended myself," he has said, "by saying my movies aren't sentimental, they just have sentiment. I feel pity for my characters." He acknowledges, however, that the line between the two is a fine one.

Bob and Carol and Ted and Alice was Mazursky's first look at life-styles. It focused on the West Coast because that was where he was living at the time. He has said that the film is "about the sexual revolution and the problems the middle class has in adjusting to a new freedom." It is the story of a filmmaker and his wife, Bob and Carol (Robert Culp and Natalie Wood), who spend a weekend at an encounter group and return home eager to share their new sexual liberation and openness with their uptight friends, Ted and Alice (Elliott Gould and Dyan Cannon).

At first, when the two couples talk at dinner, it's just talk to Ted and Alice. Ted jokingly confesses his deep feeling that Bob should pick up the check. Later, Bob returns from a business trip and confesses to Carol that he has had a casual affair. It takes her a moment to respond as she now thinks she should. Then she says, "Let me hear about it again. I feel closer to you than I ever have in my whole life." She shares this good news with a bewildered Ted and a horrified Alice.

Mazursky and Tucker got the idea for the film from a picture in *Time* magazine of six people sitting together naked in a tub. The photograph carried the caption, "Couples find joy." But the first draft of the script went very slowly until Mazursky and his wife attended an encounter session themselves. He wrote about their experience, "began to fantasize," and finished the script in five days.

Although Mazursky insisted on directing the film himself, he admitted that he had no technical experience. "What I really had," he has said, "was an instinct for staging because I had directed in the theater and been an actor. So I was able to see, for instance, that in a given scene the actors should not sit on the couch for five pages, so maybe here she should get up, go over to the bar and get a drink, and while she's getting the drink we'll put the camera over her shoulder."

He depended on his crew for technical help, but he always chose where to put the camera. For every shot in his films, Mazursky looks through the viewfinder himself. "You have to. . . . If what the camera sees is off, then your whole vision is off. So how can you work on the iceberg of the movie and leave the tip to someone else?"

Because of his experience as an actor and acting teacher, Mazursky is very comfortable working with actors, and they are comfortable with him. He has always been credited with being able to get wonderful, natural performances. He has said, "I learned something from having acted that's pragmatic—not just say it louder or do it softer. First, you must cast the part well, and then you must have a mutual kind of dialogue with the actor, where you're not afraid to admit to each other when you're stuck." During rehearsals he plays records—"anything that helps make the people more free. . . ." His sets are always relaxed, and between takes he talks and jokes.

Mazursky's acting experience also affects the way he rehearses: "Most directors don't understand the deep process of acting, whereas I know how to get actors to a relaxed place—a place where the revelations start to come. Weeks before the camera rolls, I put people together and rehearse in unusual ways." His rehearsals include going over lines and improvising character, reading the script and trying to understand it together, "then throwing the script away and just letting them talk to each other. Letting the actors trust each other enough to be silly."

He also works through surprise: "I never like to tell my actors too much of what's going on. . . . Otherwise you might get a good result, but it won't go as far as it could." At the end of *Bob and Carol*, for instance, the two couples are finally in bed together at a Las Vegas hotel after Ted has delayed in the bathroom as long as he possibly can. The actors kept asking him what they were going to do. "I really wasn't sure," Mazursky says. "But I could see that if I didn't tell them, it would add to their personal kind of dilemma, so I kept saying, 'Oh, it'll be great. It will all work out.' . . . They were all very weird and very giggly and very strange. It was real; it was happening to them." And, needless to say, the planned orgy never got off the ground.

Bob and Carol and Ted and Alice was chosen to open the New York Film Festival, the first time so clearly commercial a film did so, and it created a great controversy. Some critics found it original and funny, while others complained that it was nothing more than a slick TV situation comedy.

Despite the critical controversy, the film grossed more than $20 million and made Paul Mazursky a millionaire in a year and a half. It gave him the freedom to continue doing what he wanted in his own way. As a result, Mazursky has always had total control of his films. Not a single frame has ever been changed by a studio, and he has a voice in marketing decisions as well.

Rather than direct one of the many scripts sent to him after *Bob and Carol*, Mazursky decided to do another film based on his own background—"The people I know. The world I know. The dreams in my head. The fears in my heart." He even used his own house. This film, *Alex in Wonderland*, is about a director (Donald Sutherland) who hits it big and what happens to him in reality and in his fantasies. He doesn't want to do the scripts he is offered—*Don Quixote* as a Western, *Huckleberry Finn* as a musical, a heart transplant film—but he doesn't know what he wants to do. *Alex in Wonderland* was a critical and box office failure and marked the end of Mazursky's collaboration with Tucker.

Stephen Farber, commenting in the *New York Times*, summarized the critics' response by calling the film "an extreme in narcissistic filmmaking" and a "pop 8½." Mazursky admitted that Fellini (the director of 8½, who actually played a small part in *Alex in Wonderland*) influenced him, but claimed that he wasn't pretending to be Fellini; he "just wanted to be that good." He remains fond of *Alex* as "the infant nobody appreciated."

Mazursky was unemployed for the next two years. He had an idea for the story of an old man and a cat and got money for the first draft of a script, which he wrote with an old friend from New York. But he peddled *Harry and Tonto* around the movie studios for six months and got fourteen rejections.

Dejected, Mazursky and his family went to Europe for six months, and he almost accepted a job directing someone else's film. But at the last moment, in a mere six weeks, he wrote *Blume in Love*, which many critics consider his best film. "It was based," he has said, "on real feelings and problems I'd had with my wife in Rome. We were unhappy, we were arguing a lot. I had strange feelings. Nothing in the movie ever took place, but I guess what I wanted to write was 'What if this woman that I love so much said, "Get out!" ' "

He told the story of Steven Blume (George Segal) and his wife Nina (Susan Anspach) in flashbacks. She finds him in bed with his secretary and kicks him out. But he is obsessively in love with her and determined to get her back. "She's the only woman I will ever love," Blume says, "ever. I will die if I don't get her back. I don't want to die. Therefore I will have to get her back." In *Blume in Love*, Mazursky has said, "I wanted to deal with the middle class romantically."

Although the acting in the film was praised, some critics questioned the choice of Susan Anspach rather than an extraordinarily beautiful actress like Ali McGraw, whom the studio originally suggested for the part of Nina. "I deliberately wanted to use someone who was attractive, who tried to make her ordinariness extraordinary. The way middle-class people do," Mazursky has said, defending his choice. He also, consciously or unconsciously, chose an actress who looks strikingly like his wife.

Strangely, for a director who usually treads the same territory, Mazursky rarely uses any of the same cast. "Every part is different," he has said, "and I'm looking for the persona of that character, not just going for talent." Mazursky usually prefers to cast to type, judging less by how actors read for the part than by what he thinks they are like as people. He also has great reservations about using very famous movie stars. "Generally speaking, if you've got a big movie star in the part, the charisma of the movie star becomes greater than the reality of the role."

After the modest success of *Blume in Love*, Mazursky was able to sell *Harry and Tonto*, although the budget was pared down to the bone and he got the lowest possible fee. Yet, in spite of all the studio's hesitation, the film was praised by the critics and made $5 million.

Art Carney also won an Oscar for playing the part of Harry. Mazursky wasn't surprised. "I could tell from sitting and talking with him that he was Harry."

Harry and Tonto is the only Mazursky film critics rarely compare to his life. It is about an old man who is evicted from his New York apartment. He travels across America with his cat, meeting various characters and making disappointing stops at the homes of his three children. Mazursky has said that it is just as personal as his other films. "I got the idea for *Harry and Tonto* when I was forty. When I became forty, I began seriously to think about the fact that I would one day be seventy. When you're twenty, you'll never be seventy, but at forty, you're halfway there."

Harry and Tonto was the first film that Mazursky made entirely on location, shooting in sequence as much as possible. The cast and crew traveled across the country for nine weeks the way the character did in the script. Although this was primarily motivated by the tight budget, Mazursky actually prefers to shoot on location. He believes that the real settings add to the reality of the film and that shooting in sequence helps actors "grow with a film—get the feel of its development."

Mazursky had to return to New York for three months in 1973 to check the New York scenes of *Harry and Tonto*, which he had written from memory. After being away from it for so many years, the city looked good to him. He and his wife had adjusted to life in California, and he had even let his straight brown hair grow down to his shoulders. But he was becoming tired of California and of making movies about it. The Mazurskys decided to split their time between their house in Beverly Hills and a town house they bought in Greenwich Village. This way they could take advantage of both places—New York, which "keeps you in touch with the mob," and California, which gives you "the perpetual feeling of walking around in your underwear."

Mazursky claims that the desire to return to New York was the source of his next film, *Next Stop, Greenwich Village*: "I would literally sit down at my desk and ask, what could I write that would keep me in New York?"

The film is about Larry Lapinsky (Lenny Baker), a young man

who leaves his parents in Brooklyn to begin a life in Greenwich Village as an actor. It is also about Mazursky's friends there in the 1950s and about how he became an actor. He insists, however, that it is not the story of his youth. "I changed people around, I changed the years, I put in things I'd heard about of what happened to people I knew." Yet many details are clearly autobiographical—the Academy Award speech Larry makes to himself on the subway platform, for instance—and Mazursky has said that he wouldn't have made the film if his parents had still been alive. He has also admitted that "the boy in the movie is like me in many ways," though "he's much nicer than I was."

Mazursky is always meticulous about finding the right actors, even for minor roles. He spent six months casting *Next Stop, Greenwich Village*. He was also very careful to convey the atmosphere with correct period details: pony tails, bobby sox, old cars, old signs, old-fashioned haircuts.

Yet this funny and touching film drew mixed reviews, often for the same reasons. One critic found it "secondhand," while another said everything about it "rang a bell." Mazursky's choice of Shelley Winters for the mother was both praised and criticized, as was his choice of the late Lenny Baker as the lead. Mazursky habitually responds to criticisms, and he defended his choice of the strange-looking, gangly actor who came from Off-Broadway theater and had only minor film credits: "I really liked it that Lenny looked like some kid in the Village, not like a movie star. . . . I wanted to make the movie about people."

His next film, by contrast, got an almost unreservedly favorable reception. *An Unmarried Woman* is about thirty-seven-year-old Erica (Jill Clayburgh), an upper-middle-class wife and mother whose stockbroker husband leaves her for a younger woman after sixteen years of marriage. It is the story of her brave and successful attempt to reestablish her identity. The film was nominated for an Academy Award as best picture and won the Bodil Award of the Copenhagen Film Editors Association. Mazursky won the

National Society of Film Critics award for best screenplay and Jill Clayburgh shared the award for best actress at the Cannes Film Festival.

Mazursky spent a long time preparing this film, trying to "get inside a woman's head." He and his wife knew many women in Erica's situation, and he interviewed many more.

Before filming, he had all the women in the cast spend two weeks together doing a variety of exercises, "so they would know each other in a way that might show up on the screen." He created a history for his characters. He asked the actors to bring in their own books, records, and objects for Erica's apartment. Even the closets were filled, although their contents didn't appear on the screen. "What you see outside the frame is as important as what you see in it," he has said. He also changed the script when actresses were uncomfortable with their lines. Clayburgh contributed the bit where Erica packs up her husband's belongings and wraps them in a sheet.

As always, he kept his actors in the dark on some crucial points. For example, he didn't tell Jill Clayburgh that the woman who played the therapist Tanya in the film, in his only improvised scene, was a real psychiatrist. He also didn't tell her and Michael Murphy, who plays her husband, what would happen in the scene where he confesses to her that he has a girl friend. "I told Michael I didn't know quite what was going to happen. 'She may hit you. She may walk away.' By this time, Michael, who's a brilliant actor, was a wreck, and this fit into my design." As it turned out, Murphy bawled and Clayburgh vomited against a lamp post.

Mazursky was closely involved in the casting of this film. He spent two weeks, for instance, looking for the right actors to play Jean and Edward, an interracial couple who would appear in only two scenes and hardly speak at all. He also cast the crowd in a party scene himself, a task most directors would assign to an assistant.

His only problem with a major role was that, in the course of casting, he decided he wanted to use the British actor Alan Bates for the male lead. He had to rewrite the part to make him an Englishman who had been living in New York for about ten years.

The most serious criticism of the film was based on its difficult theme. Some critics argued that Erica's life, with her luxurious apartment and her part-time job in an art gallery, was too easy. "I deliberately did that," Mazursky answered. "I didn't want it to be a movie about a loser. . . . I wanted to show a woman who was living a pretty good life, as many are, and who'd surrendered some real parts of herself without knowing she'd done it."

Thus, he did not begrudge her in the end her romance with the charming, stable, adoring artist Saul Kaplan (Alan Bates). This character also gives Mazursky the opportunity to provide a fascinating demonstration of how an abstract painter works. Bates spent a week with Paul Jenkins, the artist whose studio and paintings are used in the film, before this scene was shot.

Although Mazursky dedicated the film in an end title to his wife, he insisted that she was not the "unmarried woman." She disagreed. "It's totally about *me*. I used to be a children's librarian, but for the past twenty years, I've been mainly at home with the children. Now I'm fifty-one and I feel the need to go back to work, to have a life of my own."

For his next film Mazursky moved away from his own generation to study the generation of the seventies. *Willie and Phil* follows three characters—two men and the woman they are both in love with—through what he sees as a decade of confusion. Some critics found the film overly sentimental, lacking the satirical bite of his other films (with its lines like "Never tell me that you love me; just love me"). Others saw it as an unsuccessful homage to François Truffaut's *Jules and Jim*, which is also about the relationships between two men and a woman. Mazursky has denied that it was a remake and said that the Truffaut film, set at

Mazursky filming *Tempest*.

the turn of the century, was only one element of his: "I am saying, in the seventies, how much it's changed . . . even though the outer form could appear to be the same."

Whatever critics said, his actors remained loyal and admiring. Margot Kidder, who played the female lead, Jeannette, said of Mazursky, "His truth meter is so precise that you can't get away with even one false moment. He demands the real you, not a battery of tricks. I've learned more from working with him than I did in twelve years of acting."

For the three weeks of rehearsal, Mazursky had the actors spend time together, often in the small Greenwich Village apartment where many of the important scenes take place. They got to know each other and, he has said, "We spent so much time there that the place got very cozy and comfortable and lived in before we ever shot a foot of film, precisely the effect I wanted."

Even after the commercial setback of *Willie and Phil*, Mazursky didn't have any trouble getting backing for his next film. Though personal, his films were familiar in style to studio executives, not dangerously avant-garde. More important, they were cheap by Hollywood standards (only *Willie and Phil* cost more than $2 million).

Mazursky is known for bringing his films in under budget. He avoids high-priced stars because he can find good actors and make them stars. He also prepares his films carefully, planning the shooting schedule and scouting locations well in advance. By the end of the pre-production period he knows what the schedule will be within a day or two and can afford to be relaxed on the set. For *Willie and Phil* he had a wall chart with the times of day and year for every interior and exterior shot.

Mazursky's next project was one he had had in mind for more than ten years—a film based loosely on Shakespeare's play *The Tempest*. "I did not feel ready for it until I finally forgot about doing it as straight Shakespeare," he has said. "Nobody will ever be able to compete in visuals with what Shakespeare does with

words." The film is about Philip, a successful, fifty-year-old architect who is in the throes of a midlife crisis. He chucks it
all—wife and job—and sets up as ruler of a lonely Greek island
with his daughter and a charming singer (Susan Sarandon) whom
he picks up in Athens. Mazursky, the successful fifty-two-year-
old filmmaker, has said that "this movie's not about me, but it's
always about me in the end."

Although the theme fits the Mazursky mold, *Tempest* is different from his other films. "I wanted to do something that I'd
never done before," he has said. "I wanted to do a movie that
would have some of the free form of Shakespeare's plays, where
almost incidentally, you have a little song, a little dance, some
low comedy, a little relief." The best instance of this occurs when
the goatherd Kalibanos (Raul Julia) with his pipe calls up the
voice of Liza Minnelli from *New York, New York* and a full
orchestra. His goats leap with joy to the music.

With a budget of $13 million, *Tempest* is also on a larger scale
than his other films. It was shot in Greece, and Mazursky hired a
special-effects artist to produce the storm. Mazursky has said he
was after the "big fish" and "you can only do that with the big
movie, the hit." Unfortunately, *Tempest* has not been a hit. The
general critical consensus was that it was "overblown."

Mazursky has already finished a draft of a new film. Perhaps
like Philip the architect, with this one he will decide to return
home again, to the smaller-scale movies that suit his themes.

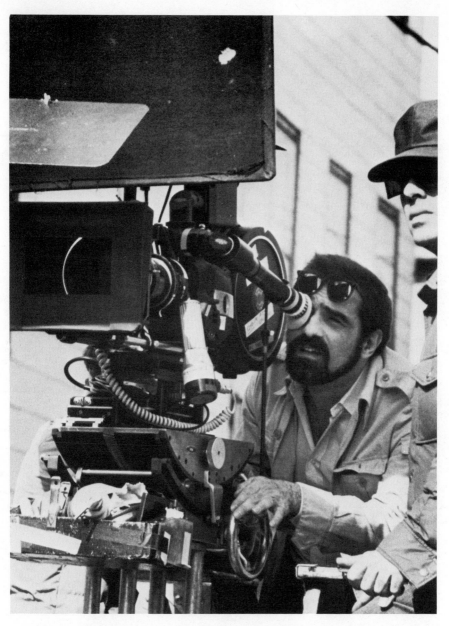

Martin Scorsese sets up a shot for *The King of Comedy*. PHOTO: Courtesy of 20th Century-Fox

Martin Scorsese

Who's That Knocking at My Door? (1967)
Boxcar Bertha (1972)
Mean Streets (1973)
Alice Doesn't Live Here Anymore (1974)
Taxi Driver (1976)
New York, New York (1977)
The Last Waltz (1978)
Raging Bull (1981)
The King of Comedy (1983)

THE SAME ADJECTIVE—"intense"—is often applied both to Martin Scorsese and to his work. This should be no surprise, for Scorsese's films are very personal. He takes characters, places, stories, and themes directly from his own life to create his films. What is perhaps surprising is that with this material he has been able to capture a public as well as a critical following.

Martin Scorsese was born on November 17, 1942, in Flushing, Queens. His parents worked in the garment industry, his father as a clothes presser, his mother as a seamstress. They had recently moved to Queens from Little Italy in Manhattan, but finances forced them to return when Marty was eight and his brother Frankie was fifteen. Scorsese grew up in a three-room tenement apartment, where his parents still live.

115

The sound and feel of the New York streets he knew so well became the sound and feel of Scorsese's films. And the undertone of violence became their undertone: "Coming home at night, it was like running an obstacle course. . . . There was always fighting going on . . . always blood in the streets. We saw fighting as the answer to most problems."

Scorsese describes his childhood as lonely; he was always an outsider. At the age of four he developed severe asthma, a condition from which he still suffers. He wasn't able to keep up with the other kids physically, and he wasn't very popular. They nicknamed him Marty Pills because of all the medication he took. Marty, unlike the guys in *Mean Streets*, didn't "hang out" much. Some of the details in that film—the fight scene in the poolroom, for instance—came to him secondhand: "I came home from school at three and sat at the kitchen table making up stories on my drawing board or watching TV or escaping to the movies . . . not being able to play ball or to fight. So I went off in the other direction, as chronicler of the group, trying to be a nice guy to have around." His poor health may also be one source of his intensity: "I'm convinced I have very little time left— physically. I just believe it. And I've got to do what's important."

Religion—Catholicism—played a big part in Scorsese's early life, and as a result, his characters are concerned with the existence of God, guilt and redemption, and humanity's ultimate end. As a boy, he wouldn't eat meat on Friday and he believed that he would go to hell if he missed Sunday mass. He entered a junior seminary and was crushed when he was expelled for bad behavior. Scorsese continued to dream of becoming "an ordinary parish priest" until he was rejected by a college divinity program and found his true vocation—film—at New York University.

Today Scorsese no longer practices Catholicism and considers himself an agnostic. But he talks about a legacy of guilt: "I've never gotten over the ritual of Catholicism." He left the Church not long after his first marriage, to a half-Jewish, half-Irish girl in

1965. "There were problems about mortal sin, certain sexual things. But what *really* did it was sitting in a church in Los Angeles and hearing a priest call the Vietnam War a holy war."

Scorsese has a very close, warm relationship with his parents, as is obvious from *Italianamerican*, the documentary he made about them in 1974. In their apartment, they talk about the old days, as Catherine Scorsese makes her spaghetti sauce. His parents also have bit parts in some of his other films.

The Scorseses are proud of their son and have always supported his career. "There were times when he was working at NYU when I used to get into a cab and bring him some food and then wait to make sure he ate it," his mother has said. His father scraped up the money for his first short films and took out student loans to support his first feature.

It was also his father who got him hooked on movies at an early age. They went to the movies together at least three times a week. Then, when Marty got home, he would draw detailed sequences from the films, frame by frame, color them in, and pull them through a cardboard movie screen. Now he draws sketches for his own films. Most of them are at least partly worked out scene by scene with all the camera angles before they are shot.

As a boy, he also staged epics on the roof of his apartment building. One he actually filmed, based on his script and storyboards, and accompanied with a tape of dialogue and music. *Vesuvius VIII*, a parody of the television series "Surfside 6," was set in ancient Rome because sheets were the only costumes available.

The films Scorsese saw while growing up provide a lodestone of images on which he can draw. He still keeps lists called "Movies I Saw This Year," which he began in childhood, and his own films are crammed with references to and even clips from his favorites. "I will always have things about movies in my movies," he has said. "I can't help it. I love movies—it's my whole life and that's it."

Asked by a film magazine what films he loved most, Scorsese almost couldn't restrain himself. He listed one hundred, some of which he's seen more than forty times, and said, "Those weren't all." The films that most influenced him, he said, are *Scorpio Rising, Duel in the Sun,* and the Westerns of John Ford. Elsewhere he commented on directors. "The director I feel closest to is [Samuel] Fuller, his camera movement, his aggressiveness, the emotional and physical impact of his films."

Scorsese graduated from NYU in 1964 and from its graduate school of film in 1967. He taught there while he was a graduate student and also during the two years after he got his degree. He credits NYU mainly with giving him the opportunity to use equipment and to make films. He directed five films in his time there, all of which won awards.

One of these—*Who's That Knocking at My Door?*—became his first feature. It's the story of J.R., an Italian Catholic boy who falls in love with a girl from a different world: she reads foreign magazines, lives alone, and—most important—has been raped. He can't break away from his upbringing enough to accept her when he finds this out.

This early film contains many of the basic elements of Scorsese's style. It has a loose structure and an improvisational look. The sound track is filled with rock music, and he combines a hand-held camera, zooms, and tracking movements with tight, fast editing. There are also film references: at the couple's first meeting, they discuss John Ford's *The Searchers.* Only Scorsese's characteristic violence is missing from this film.

Scorsese made the film for $35,000, most of which was raised by one of his teachers at NYU. It took two years, on and off, to shoot and another two years to find a distributor. The one they finally found took the film on the condition (which Scorsese accepted) that a sex scene be added, even though the girl in the scene appears nowhere else in the film. The reviews were respectful, but not enthusiastic.

During all this time, Scorsese took on various odd jobs in films to keep food on the table. He was an editor of news film at CBS, he made commercials in Europe, he worked on John Cassavetes's *Minnie and Moskowitz*. He also was supervising editor of the rock film *Woodstock* and accomplished the extraordinary feat of shaping more than one hundred hours of film into three.

In 1971 he went to Hollywood to edit *Medicine Ball Caravan*, another rock film. There he met Roger Corman, king of blood-and-gore exploitation films. Corman had liked *Who's That Knocking at My Door?* and asked Scorsese to direct *Boxcar Bertha*, the sequel to his *Bloody Mama*. The film is about a couple during the depression who meet their doom fighting the railroad bosses.

Corman told Scorsese that he could make the film any way he wanted so long as it had the right proportions of action, nudity, and violence and so long as he spent no more than twenty-four days on location in Kansas. Scorsese used his sharp eye for period detail and locale well and filled the film with references to action-adventure movies. It received some favorable reviews (the *New York Times* critic called it "beautifully directed"), but *Variety*'s critic wrote, "*Boxcar Bertha* is not much more than an excuse to slaughter a lot of people."

In a long conversation after the filming of *Boxcar Bertha*, John Cassavetes persuaded Scorsese not to go on with Corman but to try to return to personal filmmaking. Scorsese dug out an old script he had begun with a classmate at NYU and with unaccountable good luck met an enthusiastic novice producer at a dinner party. Suddenly he had $550,000 and twenty-seven days to make *Mean Streets*, although he could afford only six of these on location in New York. The rest was shot in Los Angeles.

The main character of the film, Charlie, is a direct outgrowth of J.R. in *Who's That Knocking at My Door?* and is played by the same actor, Harvey Keitel. Charlie is also, in some sense, Scorsese himself. He has said that he was "compelled" to make this film and that it was a "purging" for him: "The conflicts within Charlie were within me, my own feelings.

Mean Streets is the story of a would-be saint who is caught between loyalty to his girl friend Teresa and his crazed, self-destructive friend Johnny Boy (Robert De Niro) on the one side; and on the other side by his desire to rise in his gangster uncle's local racketeering organization. The Church is important to Charlie, and he knows he is a sinner, but he constantly reminds God that he is trying. He also keeps testing hell's fires by sticking his finger into a flame.

The plot meanders, its incidents revolving around Johnny Boy, who irresponsibly has defaulted on his payments to a loan shark. He doesn't even offer excuses. It turns out at last that Charlie has overestimated himself: he can't be everything to everybody. He tries to drive his friends to safety and instead heads them into a blast of gunfire.

The setting in Little Italy is straight from Scorsese's childhood. In fact, some of the scenes were shot in his parents' home. He has also said that 95 percent of the story actually happened. But the film is personal on another level, too. "When I first wrote it," he has said, "it was like an allegory for what was happening to me trying to make movies. . . . I drew from personal experiences about a guy trying to make it."

The pulsating, loud score of *Mean Streets* attests to Scorsese's lifelong passion for music. Today his traveling tape collection includes the opera *Don Giovanni*, and he keeps his radio tuned to rock 'n' roll. He carefully selected about twenty-five songs for the film, a conflicting combination of sixties rock and traditional Italian music. The feeling of potential violence is emphasized by the red lighting in the bar and the use of a hand-held camera.

The film's small budget allowed the cast only ten days of rehearsal time. "The characters and attitudes were basic to all of us," Scorsese has said. Keitel had played J.R., and Robert De Niro (Johnny Boy) comes from a background similar to Scorsese's. Other major characters were played by New York, and many of the extras were old friends of Scorsese's who just happened to be hanging around. There were only three or four improvisations on camera, but during rehearsal some improvisations were videotaped and written into the script—a technique Scorsese uses in all of his films.

Scorsese himself plays two roles in *Mean Streets*: he speaks the first line ("You don't pay for your sins in church, but in the streets"), and he is the one who pulls the trigger on Charlie and his friends as they are trying to escape.

Perhaps too disturbing for most audiences, *Mean Streets* did not do very well at the box office. The reviews, however, were adulatory. The big question remained: would Martin Scorsese be able to do it again, with other stories in other settings?

He took the challenge head on with *Alice Doesn't Live Here Anymore*, a witty film about a woman from a New Mexico suburb. Alice Hyatt (Ellen Burstyn) is set free from a stifling marriage by the death of her truck-driver husband. She and her wisecracking son hit the road for Monterey, where she hopes to fulfill her childhood dream of becoming a singer. The fact that she settles down in the end with a comfortable rancher (Kris Kristofferson) inflamed some feminist critics. But Scorsese answered that this was not intended to be a feminist film and that "Alice needs a relationship with a man. That's her character."

Nevertheless, he had hired women for key production roles and consulted them constantly about whether the emotions in the film were accurate. And one reason he gave for deciding to make the film was: "I wanted to better understand my relationships with women."

By this time Scorsese had married, had a daughter, and been divorced. He was living with the associate producer of *Alice*. That romance ended, and in 1975 he married Julia Cameron, a journalist, and had another daughter. When that marriage also ended, he married Isabella Rossellini in 1979, the daughter of

Ingrid Bergman and filmmaker Roberto Rossellini. They are now divorced.

Warner Brothers gave Scorsese a budget of $1.6 million for *Alice*. This allowed him to spend $85,000 to create a summer evening set for a flashback. In the beginning he shows Alice as a little girl who "wants to sing just as good as Alice Faye," in a scene recalling *The Wizard of Oz*. The budget also gave him time to rehearse and to improvise. The actors experimented with their lines in front of a videotape machine and sent the results to the screenwriter for approval or rewrite. Harvey Keitel, who plays Alice's psychotic lover Ben and has been in most of Scorsese's films, has talked about working with him, "Marty lets actors bring their own humanity—their eccentricities, their humor, their compassion—to a role. With Marty you have freedom, and you know something always pops up."

Although *Alice* is a film completely different in tone from *Mean Streets* (one reason he was attracted to it), it is still recognizably Scorsese's. He continued to use a hand-held camera a great deal. One reason he gave for this was that he often filmed action in very small rooms. Also, he has said, "I wanted to suggest a psychological uneasiness in the character or drop a hint of what was coming in order to make the audience feel subconsciously uneasy." He does this, for instance, before the jarringly violent scene when Ben bursts in on Alice.

The score, also, is carefully thought out. "The choice of music," Scorsese has said, "came from the characters' heads." Alice listens to songs like "Where or When" and "I've Got a Crush on You," and her son listens to rock 'n' roll.

Although reviews were mixed and some critics dismissed the film as just another cotton candy romance, it was a box office hit, and Ellen Burstyn (Alice) won an Oscar for best actress. Scorsese has been accused of selling out to Hollywood with *Alice*, but he insists that it is a highly personal film: "The feelings, the emotions, and the situations are pretty similar to things I am going through or have gone through. . . . *Alice* is from my life; it's just not blatant."

In 1974, just before filming *Alice*, Scorsese made a blatantly personal film, *Italianamerican*, the affectionate, moving documentary about his parents. It received a standing ovation when it was shown at the New York Film Festival.

Scorsese's next film was *Taxi Driver*, the story of a crazy New York City cab driver, Travis Bickle, played by Robert De Niro. Travis sees only the ugliness of the city as he drives at night—the physical and human debris. He is alienated and ready to explode with violence at anything. He assembles an arsenal of guns, exercises his body, and even gives himself a Mohawk haircut in preparation for assassinating a political candidate. When that fails, he feels compelled to rescue Iris, a twelve-year-old prostitute, from her pimp.

Another "false saint," like Charlie, Scorsese said, "the guy sets out to save people who don't want to be saved and ends up hurting them." He also said, "I know this guy Travis. I've had the feelings he has. . . . I know the feeling of rejection that Travis feels, of not being able to make relationships survive. I know . . . the feeling of really being angry."

Scorsese plays a small role in the film, a passenger who orders Travis to stop outside an apartment building where he says his wife is having an affair with a black man. He describes in brutal detail how he is going to kill her. Although Scorsese denies that he is an actor, Pauline Kael wrote in the *New Yorker* that his scene "burns a small hole in the screen."

Scorsese stayed much closer to this script than to the others, and only three or four scenes in the film are improvised. But according to the screenwriter, Paul Schrader, "Marty's not an easy person to work with. . . . One of the reasons that Marty's good is that he's headstrong and stubborn, he has a very strong view of himself. . . . Therefore, he often takes criticism as a child takes a beating, wincing at every blow."

In *Taxi Driver*, Scorsese brilliantly evokes the hot, dirty streets of a New York summer. The score, with its sense of doom, is by Bernard Herrmann, whose dissonant music is known for suggesting psychological disorder. Oddly, though, there is not one hand-held shot in the film. "The subject matter is so strong in *Taxi Driver*," Scorsese has said, "that the camera movements don't have to take over . . . but the funny thing is, no hand-held shots and the picture still looks like a documentary."

Tension builds in the film until the bloody ending, when Travis shoots Iris's pimp and all the other seedy characters around. There was much controversy over this scene, but Scorsese insists that it is necessary to provide release for the audience: "If you are going to deal with violence, it has got to be cathartic." Threatened with an X rating, however, Scorsese toned down the red of the spurting blood.

To everyone's surprise, the critical and financial success of *Taxi Driver* was even greater than that of *Alice*, and the film won top prize at the Cannes Film Festival in 1976.

One sad footnote was the role *Taxi Driver* apparently played in the attempted assassination of President Reagan in 1981. John W. Hinckley, Jr., claimed to have seen the film at least fifteen times and in many ways modeled himself on Travis Bickle—from his clothes to his diary to his obsession with "Iris." Hinckley said that he wanted to impress Jodie Foster, who played the young prostitute. He phoned and wrote her and even followed her around her college campus. After he was convicted, he said that he likes to think that he "altered her life forever."

In 1975, Martin Scorsese gave this formula for surviving in Hollywood: "If you can take on a variety of commercially appealing movies, movies you can learn from, and every once in a while sandwich in a labor of love, like *Taxi Driver*, you're doing okay." *New York, New York* was meant to be his "commercially appealing movie," a homage to the Hollywood musicals of the 1940s and early 1950s. He researched his subject painstakingly, viewing again all the more dramatic musicals of that period. United Artists gave him a budget of more than $9 million, which he spent on period sets, period costumes, and six hundred extras. He also spent $350,000 on a single production number.

Scorsese had said before he made the film, "I wanted to make a big commercial Hollywood movie, and still get my theme across." That theme is the relationship of two people who are in love but can't make it work. Francine Evans (Liza Minnelli) is a singer of popular music ("as sweet as she sings, that's how sweet she is," her manager gushes). Jimmy Doyle (Robert De Niro) is a temperamental jazz saxophonist. Her career soars, his doesn't.

There were problems with the screenplay, and Scorsese finally shot with only a story outline, using videotaped improvisations to rewrite the script. He said afterward that *New York, New York* "turned out to be one of the most personal films I've ever made." The movies of the forties remind him of his uncles in uniform.

Also, years later, he realized "that in making that film I was chronicling the painful disintegration of my own marriage." His wife, like Jimmy Doyle's, was pregnant, and thus his art, like Doyle's, was "on the line." There were also rumors of a romance between him and his star.

New York, New York was far from a success, commercially or critically. Some reviewers thought that the original genre was not interesting enough to warrant so much attention. Others didn't like the abrasive edge of the film (in one scene, for instance, Doyle strikes his pregnant wife). Musical fans couldn't have a good time. Re-released in 1981, however, the film fared much better with the critics.

While still polishing *New York*, Scorsese directed Liza Minnelli in a play called *The Act*, which was vaguely intended to be an extension of the movie. He had no theatrical experience and made some bad beginner's mistakes. The play sold out because of Minnelli's drawing power but was a critical disaster, and Scorsese was replaced as director.

Meanwhile, he had already begun working on *The Last Waltz*, which has been called the best rock film ever made. It is a documentary of the last concert given by The Band in the fall of 1976, when they shared the stage with all the great rock stars of the seventies. Scorsese outdid even his usually thorough planning. Each page of the shooting script was divided into columns for singer, lyrics, tone, lighting, and camera; everything was precisely choreographed.

During this same hectic period, he shot *American Boy*, a short documentary about his friend and business associate Steve Prince, which was never released. "I like to do documentaries while I do features," Scorsese has said, "to keep my hand in. That's when you go back to the roots."

Scorsese described his next film, *Raging Bull*, also as being close to the roots. It is the story of the rise and fall of Jake La Motta, world middleweight boxing champion of 1949. When Robert De Niro first brought La Motta's autobiography to Scorsese, he resisted. Then he began to see some of his own themes in the story of "a guy attaining something and losing everything, and then redeeming himself." The violence of this man's life—both in the ring and at home—also struck a familiar note.

Two different screenwriters worked on the script. But in the end Scorsese and De Niro, who had been talking it through for two months, went off for ten days to a Caribbean island to write it together.

Scorsese said that he wanted the film to be "real" above all else. With precision, he re-created the details of the New York Italian neighborhoods of the 1940s. He did research in gyms and boxing stadiums. "I was struck by two images," he has said, "the bloody sponges and the blood dripping from the ropes, and I used them in the film."

He deliberately cast nonprofessionals and unfamiliar actors whose style suited his and De Niro's conception of the characters. Joe Pesci, who played Jake's brother, had made only one film, which they had seen, and was working as a restaurant manager. Pesci saw Cathy Moriarty's photograph in a disco slide show and was struck by her resemblance to Vickie, Jake's wife. Scorsese tested her for three months—her only acting experience—then gave her the role. He hired fighters, trainers, and ring announcers for small parts.

The most awesome element of realism, however, was provided by Robert De Niro. His role spanned La Motta's life from the trim young fighter of the 1940s and 1950s to the obese, pathetic nightclub personality of the 1960s. In addition to working out in a gym with La Motta every day for a year, De Niro spent a four-month break in the filming gaining fifty-five pounds.

Scorsese shot *Raging Bull* in black and white. He wanted to recall viewers' memories of boxing in the forties and fifties, which are mainly from black-and-white films. Scorsese is also very concerned about the problem of color film fading. The color film that most filmmakers use is unstable. In as little as ten years, the blues and yellows begin to disappear, leaving only a pinkish purple. For the past few years Scorsese has led a campaign to force Eastman Kodak and the studios to do something about this.

Raging Bull was controversial. Some critics called it a masterful achievement, while others faulted it for lacking motivation. Nevertheless, it won two Academy Awards—for best actor and best editing—and was nominated for six others, including best director.

Scorsese's newest film, *The King of Comedy*, opened to mixed reviews. It is the story of an aspiring comic, Rupert Pupkin (Robert De Niro) who, in an attempt to get his big break on TV, kidnaps his idol, a talk show host played by Jerry Lewis. Scorsese has said of him: "Rupert's an extension of me inasmuch as he'd do *anything* to get what he wanted. . . . He was to comics as I was to the movies. . . . Rupert reminds me of the hunger I had in the sixties." He has also said that the film is about "a person's right to be by himself, within himself," something Scorsese

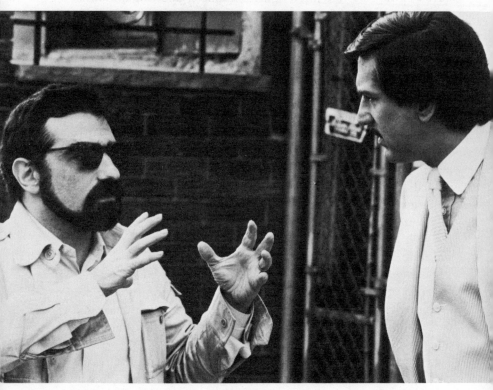

Scorsese discusses a scene in *The King of Comedy* with Robert De Niro.
PHOTO: Courtesy of 20th Century-Fox

understands after years of being a celebrity in the film industry.

With this film, as with his others, Martin Scorsese seems to be aiming for a personal goal. "I want to communicate on the basic human level," he once said, "sad, funny, violent, painful. I don't want to do movies unless they further me not only as a filmmaker but as a person."

Steven Spielberg directing *E.T.*

Steven Spielberg

The Sugarland Express (1974)
Jaws (1975)
Close Encounters of the Third Kind (1977)
1941 (1979)
Raiders of the Lost Ark (1981)
Poltergeist (1982, executive producer)
E.T. The Extra-Terrestrial (1982)

STEVEN SPIELBERG, at the age of thirty-five, is the director of four of the top-grossing movies of all time. He has been described as an instinctive movie craftsman and, like other personal directors in Hollywood, is involved in his films from their conception through their release. He has also been described as a "popcorn" director, which doesn't embarrass him at all. "I think that popular movies that are well made are an indication that you're not working in a vacuum," he has said, and "I never want to stop entertaining."

Spielberg started entertaining as a child. He was born in Cincinnati on December 18, 1947, and was uprooted several times as his father, a computer engineer, took jobs at different electronics firms in New Jersey, Arizona, and finally California (when Steven was seventeen). He has said that he was a "wimp" as a child, a skinny kid with big ears, who couldn't play sports and couldn't

131

fix cars. "I was a loner and very lonely. I was the only Jewish kid in school, and I was very shy and uncertain." It was not until high school that he found fellow spirits—in the theater arts program. "That's when I realized there were options besides being a jock or a wimp."

At home he applied his theatrical gifts to torturing his three younger sisters. He would tell them bedtime horror stories, then after they were asleep, go to their window with a flashlight and call, "I am the moo-oo-oo-oon."

Spielberg's mother was a former concert pianist, and she arranged music lessons for him at an early age. He now considers music his "second love" and has a vast collection of sound track recordings. His parents were very strict about television and movies, however. On TV he saw only Soupy Sales, Sid Caesar, and "The Honeymooners." Although he occasionally sneaked out to movies like *I Was a Teenage Werewolf*, he usually went with his parents to general audience features or Disney cartoons. It wasn't until he was a professional filmmaker that he began to see the great classics. He still does not consider himself a film scholar.

Spielberg became involved in films more from doing than from seeing. The Spielbergs often went backpacking and camping in the woods together, and he was in charge of the family's home movies. "I began actually to stage the camping trips and later cut the bad footage out," he has said. Spielberg's first films were *Father Chopping Wood, Mother Digging Latrine, Young Sister Removing Fishhook From Right Eye,* and *Bear in the Bushes*. "Sometimes I would just have fun and shoot two frames of this and three frames of that and ten frames of something else, and it got to the point where the documentaries were more surrealistic than factual."

Soon he began making 8-millimeter silent movies. He wrote the scripts, drew the storyboards for hours alone in his room, and used neighborhood kids in the cast. Most of these were horror films, a rebellion against his parents' strictness, and involved buckets of blood. He would charge 25¢ admission to cover the costs.

At thirteen, Spielberg earned a Boy Scout merit badge in photography with a three-minute Western he made called *The Last Gun*. When he showed the film to the troop, "I got whoops and screams and applause and everything else that made me want it more and more." Other Westerns and war films followed, growing more technically sophisticated. At fifteen, Spielberg won first prize in an amateur film festival for a fifteen-minute war picture called *Escape to Nowhere*.

At sixteen, he wrote, directed, shot, and edited a two-and-a-half-hour 8-millimeter sound feature called *Firelight*. Like his later film, *Close Encounters of the Third Kind*, it is about a team of scientists investigating mysterious lights in the sky. His father bankrolled about $300 of the $500 budget. The rest Steven earned by whitewashing citrus trees for 75¢ apiece. He made it all back and cleared $50 in a one-night showing at a rented theater.

When the group assembled to see the movie, Spielberg said, "I knew what I wanted. . . . I wanted Hollywood." But his grades were too low for him to get into any college with a film program. He went to California State at Long Beach, which didn't even have a film history course ("just to be close to Hollywood") and nominally majored in English. What he actually did was make films and go constantly to movie theaters and student film festivals. He also claims that for three months he dressed up in a suit and, carrying a briefcase, walked unnoticed into an empty office on the Universal lot, where he could watch directors and editors at work.

During college he made many short 16-millimeter films, which he has described as "very esoteric." His break came when a young would-be producer arranged to get him $10,000 to make a twenty-four-minute film called *Amblin'*, about a boy and a girl who meet in the Mojave Desert and hitchhike together to the Pacific Ocean. It won awards at film festivals in Atlanta and Venice and so impressed the president of Universal's television division that he gave Spielberg a seven-year contract.

Yet Spielberg has called the film a "Pepsi commercial" and said that it "was a conscious effort to break into the business and become successful by proving to people I could move a camera and compose nicely and deal with lighting and performances. The only challenge that's close to my heart about *Amblin'* is I was able to tell a story about a boy and a girl with no dialogue. That was something I set out to do before I found out I couldn't afford sound even if I wanted it."

At the age of twenty-one, Steven Spielberg began his career as a television director by directing a show starring Joan Crawford. He made ten episodes in all for series that included "Marcus Welby," "The Psychiatrists," and "Columbo." He also made three television movies before he went on to direct feature films. He has said that he took his TV work seriously, worrying about composition and aspect ratios on every shot: "I considered each show a mini-feature. . . . I refused to conform to . . . the television formula of closeup, two-shot, over-the-shoulder, and master shot."

Spielberg doesn't regret his television experience at all. "Television has taught me to imagine the finished product," he has said, "and then just before shooting retrace my thoughts and follow that imaginary blueprint . . . because you're making an hour show in six days. You better know line for line, shot for shot exactly what you're doing."

His care on *Duel*, a television movie based on a short story, paid off. *Duel* is the story of a mild-mannered traveling salesman whose red Plymouth Valiant is pursued by a gasoline truck with an unseen driver intent on destroying him. This is a theme that reappears in Spielberg's work: the ordinary man who rises to heroism when he has to confront a menacing force.

Duel was shot in sixteen days for $425,000, and Spielberg has said that it was a much greater challenge than the big-budget *Jaws*: "Trying to create that kind of fear out of a truck is a lot harder than the established fear of a man-eating fish underwater." The film was released in theaters in Europe, where it earned Universal $9 million and won several prestigious awards.

After *Duel*, Spielberg got many feature film offers, including the chance to direct *White Lightning*, a Burt Reynolds picture. He had worked on it for two and a half months before he realized that he "didn't want to start my career as a hardhat journeyman director. I wanted to do something that was a little more personal." He took off a year and wrote a twenty-page treatment for *Sugarland Express*. It was based on a newspaper story about a young criminal and his wife. They kidnapped a policeman and drove across Texas with him in search of their baby, who was taken away by the welfare department.

Spielberg went back to television work and then, two years later, hired two writers to make his treatment into a screenplay, which Richard Zanuck and David Brown produced for Universal. Spielberg has said that the film "made an important statement about the Great American Dream Machine that can transform two innocent people into celebrities." Although some reviewers doubted whether it was saying that—or anything else—it was, nevertheless, a critical success. The performances were praised (Goldie Hawn's Lou Jean was said to be the best role of her career); the choreography of the two hundred and fifty cars that followed the fugitives was said to be masterly; and the screenplay won an award at Cannes. Pauline Kael wrote in the *New Yorker*: "In terms of the pleasure that technical assurance gives an audience, this film is one of the most phenomenal debut films in the history of movies."

Sugarland Express only just broke even at the box office. Its producers were impressed enough with Spielberg, however, that when he asked to direct a movie based on a novel he had picked up in their office, they agreed. That novel was *Jaws*. This is the story of a summer beach community that is terrorized by the appearance near shore of a man-eating shark. It is also about the greedy local authorities who try to hide the truth to save the tourist trade.

In the last part, which attracted Spielberg, three men who have little in common—a tough old sea dog (Robert Shaw), a wealthy ichthyologist (Richard Dreyfuss), and the town's New York–bred police chief (Roy Scheider)—go out in a boat together to hunt the shark. Only two return, but they kill the shark.

The shark itself doesn't appear until more than an hour into the film. Instead, low, growling chords play and the camera zigzags underwater to indicate its presence. Spielberg deliberately used this device, which he insisted on as soon as he read the manuscript, to build tension and suspense.

Jaws was a very difficult film to make, and in the course of production, the budget doubled to $8 million. The most persistent problems were the unpredictable weather and the unreliable mechanical sharks, all nicknamed Bruce, after Spielberg's lawyer. But there were others. Because of an impending actors' strike, Spielberg was given only three and a half months to prepare, instead of the year he said he needed. He usually sketches every shot of his films in stick figures, from which an artist does the detailed drawings of the storyboards. For *Jaws*, he could do this only for the last part. The rest was planned a week or a day in advance, or even on the set. "I did not begin *Jaws* with a visual conception of the finished product—as I did *Sugarland*," he has said. There was also no time for rehearsing the actors. The cast wasn't even together when shooting began, and some of the small parts were cast as they came up.

The screenplay was another major problem. There were six drafts and five writers, including Spielberg, and the result was "a script I didn't care for and had to improvise my way through." The actors, he has said, "contributed more to their dialogue than any of the writers." They went through each day's dialogue at Spielberg's house the evening before. A writer would be there to take down the improvisations that worked well.

Spielberg has always had a good rapport with his actors, perhaps because he acted in high-school plays and took two years of acting classes. Richard Dreyfuss, who starred in both *Jaws* and *Close Encounters of the Third Kind,* has said that Spielberg is a good director to work with "because, unlike some directors, he actually *knows* what he wants." Dreyfuss has also said, "Steve's not what you would call an actor's director in the classical sense. But he's relaxed and open in the way he communicates what he wants, and he helps you to get there."

"The most important thing about a film," Spielberg has said, "is the story." But he likes to give actors enough freedom so that "they can show me things that I didn't come prepared to show them." There are only two things that he is a tyrant about— "where to put the camera and where to make the splice." He is also a perfectionist, who will shoot scenes over and over until they satisfy him. And he never considers a film finished until he has previewed it before a real audience. Three weeks before *Jaws* was to open, he discovered at a preview that two of what were supposed to be the scariest moments didn't work as well as they should have: when a dead man's head pops out of a hole in a sunken boat's hull and when the shark first leaps out of the water. He edited again and used his own money to shoot new underwater footage in a swimming pool.

Most critics reviewed *Jaws* as a well-crafted scare movie, but nothing more. Spielberg himself has said of it, "Lots of filmmakers want to do something important. There's great validity in wanting to do something that enriches someone else's life. But there's also nothing wrong with a fast-food movie if it's done with skill and affection and honesty. And *Jaws* was that kind of picture."

The film grossed $400 million, more than any other film at

that time, and the Hollywood studios were impressed. When Spielberg turned down the opportunity to direct the sequel for Universal, Columbia executives told him he could make whatever movie he wanted at whatever cost. He chose *Close Encounters of the Third Kind,* which he had conceived before *Jaws.*

Spielberg has said that the film about contact with extraterrestrials was "a personal statement out of my own head." He related it to his childhood, when he would look up into the clear Arizona skies through his homemade reflecting telescope. He also clearly remembered his father, a science fiction buff, waking him up in the middle of the night and driving him to a far-off field to see a spectacular meteor shower.

Spielberg spent a year doing research, reading about UFOs, and also interviewing people who had had extraordinary experiences. In fact, the appearance of the chief alien, designed by Carlo Rambaldi (who also designed E.T.), was based on people's reports.

He then wrote the screenplay himself. He doesn't consider himself a writer and prefers to collaborate with others, but in the case of *Close Encounters,* he has said, "I couldn't find anybody who would write it the way I wanted" (as a combination adventure story and personal story).

Close Encounters is the story of Roy Neary (Richard Dreyfuss), an electrical worker from Muncie, Indiana, who is seared by a blinding light and experiences strange phenomena while driving his truck one night. He becomes obsessed by the vision of a mountain, which he sculpts out of shaving cream and food. When he starts to build a model out of soil he has shoveled into the living room, his family finally abandons him. It is also the story of Jillian Guiler (Melinda Dillon), similarly obsessed, whose three-year-old son was spirited away. Both, along with other ordinary people, are drawn to Devils Tower in Wyoming, where a team of scientists is calling a spaceship with a five-note musical greeting. Their awesome encounter fills the last forty minutes of the film.

Close Encounters took two years to make, including five months of shooting. For this film, Spielberg planned every scene in detail on storyboards, producing more than fifteen hundred drawings. He has said that this preparation enhances rather than restricts his spontaneity. "I'm almost at my most improvisatory when I've planned most thoroughly, when my storyboards are in continuity."

There were countless headaches in this film also, and the budget escalated from $12 million to $18 million in the course of filming. The locations ranged from California to India, but most of it had to be shot in a huge World War II air force hangar outside Mobile, Alabama, which is six times larger than any sound stage. There were 350 special effects, engineered by a crew of more than forty animators, model makers, matte artists, optical-effects specialists, and electronics engineers. Spielberg designed and directed the special effects himself, overseeing all the photography and every element that went into a final shot. He even drilled the window holes in part of the mothership.

Since Spielberg was determined to surprise audiences with these special effects, he kept tight security on the shooting site. No one could get past the guards without an identification badge, and everyone working on the film had to take a vow of silence.

The cast included the French filmmaker François Truffaut, as the gurulike head scientist. Although he had never before acted in a film other than his own, Truffaut was working on a book called *The Actor*, and he wanted the experience of being directed. He said later that he was pleasantly surprised at the performance that Spielberg coaxed out of him.

Spielberg spent more than a year editing *Close Encounters*. Editing is the part of filmmaking that he enjoys the most, does best, and considers "the most creative part of filmmaking." The editors he works with are "just sort of completing my vision. I'm stopping the moviola on a signal frame and saying, 'Mark here.'"

Close Encounters, with its optimistic vision of extraterrestrial contact as opposed to the standard attack from outer space, got mainly enthusiastic reviews, and Spielberg was nominated for an Academy Award as best director. The major criticism was that the center part of the film was weak. Taking this to heart, Spielberg asked the studio for $1 million to make a "Special Edition" of the film, which was released in 1980. He tightened the middle and changed the ending, so that the audience gets to see the inside of the spaceship.

What followed his two blockbusters (*Close Encounters* made $250 million), was Spielberg's only total disaster, both critical and commercial. His *1941* is a comedy, starring the late actor John Belushi, about the panic that hit California after Pearl Harbor was bombed, when the citizens of Los Angeles thought they would be the next target. The film took two hectic and difficult years to make and cost $30 million.

"I had always wanted to try a visual comedy," Spielberg has said, "but with enough adventure and action where I felt that I'd be sort of in my own element and not out in the cold." He also enjoyed the studio shooting. Much of the budget had gone into building a set of the Los Angeles of forty years ago. "There was a real sense of the old tinseltown on a Hollywood sound stage."

He admitted, however, that "comedy is not my forte," and, unfortunately the critics agreed that the film was just not funny.

Analyzing his mistakes later, Spielberg has said, "Until then I thought I was immune to failure. But I couldn't come down from the power high of making big films on large canvases. I threw everything in, and it killed the soup: *1941* was my encounter with economic reality." He learned his lesson well. After three films that went substantially over budget, Spielberg made three films that were not only on budget but ahead of schedule.

The first of these, *Raiders of the Lost Ark*, was a collaboration with George Lucas, who had been a friend for eleven years. The film, a nonstop adventure that recalls the movie serials of the thirties and forties, was Lucas's idea. He and Spielberg both contributed to the writing of Lawrence Kasden's screenplay, beginning with five nine-hour days of hammering out the story together.

Set in 1936, it is about an adventurous professor of archaeology, Indiana Jones (played by Harrison Ford, who was Han Solo in *Star Wars*). He is sent by U.S. Intelligence in search of the lost Ark of the Covenant, a chest containing the original tablets of the Ten Commandments and with them the power of God. It is a race between him and Hitler's archaeologists. And the action never stops, whether Jones is risking his life in a daredevil truck chase or in a room filled with eight thousand snakes.

The film was shot in four countries on three continents and had forty optical effects, but Spielberg ran a tight ship. About 80 percent of *Raiders* was on storyboards; Spielberg had made 2,700 sketches of the scenes before shooting. He did an average of four takes per shot, as compared with twenty in the film *1941*. There was also less improvisation, he said, because he had a better script than ever before. He decided to make "a real good B-plus film. I decided not to shoot for a masterpiece but to make a good movie that told George's story very well."

As for whose film it is, that is a close question. Spielberg has said, "I was making this movie for my friend George, for his company and for his idea. I just didn't feel that it was right to impose a lot of my own expressionism into George's style." What he contributed to the film was "more humor than it would otherwise have had." He "substituted humor and invention," he later said, "for time-consuming technique and additional angles."

Spielberg said he needed *Raiders* "to exorcise myself from a kind of rut I was falling into—where I wouldn't walk away from a shot until it was 100 percent of what I intended." The film, which grossed $310 million, opened to near unanimous raves, although Stuart Byron in a dissenting review in the *Village Voice* pointed out that "even its proponents agree it is nothing but superior entertainment."

The next two Spielberg films, *Poltergeist* and *E.T. The Extra-Terrestrial*, were very much his own, although his actual title on *Poltergeist* was executive producer (Tobe Hooper was the director). Spielberg had been an executive producer of three previous films—*I Wanna Hold Your Hand*, *Used Cars*, and *Continental Divide*—but his personal involvement in these was small. For *Poltergeist* he collaborated on the screenplay, which was based on his original story, did the storyboards, chose the cast and locations, was on the set almost every day, and supervised the final editing.

The film, which has over a hundred optical effects, is about an ordinary suburban couple whose house is haunted by ghosts. They fly out of the TV set one night and kidnap five-year-old Carol Anne. The parents finally get her back with the help of Tangina, a psychic. Spielberg has said that the film "reflects a lot of the fears I had at night—scary shadows that could simply be bunched-up clothes or a shadow like Godzilla cast by the hall light." Reviewers generally recommended it as an entertaining thriller.

Poltergeist and *E.T.*, Spielberg's next film released a few weeks later, showed off a new side of him, which led Vincent Canby to call him "the best director of children now working in American movies." He enjoys working with children, and Robert Mac-Naughton, who plays the older brother in *E.T.*, has said that he is good at "talking to kids on their own level." Spielberg now hopes that he will be taken seriously as a director of actors. Only one of his actors (Melinda Dillon in *Close Encounters*) was ever nominated for an Academy Award.

E.T. was a great step in the direction of personal filmmaking

Spielberg and Henry Thomas on location with *E.T.*

for Spielberg. It is based on his own story about an extraterrestrial being who is accidentally left on earth by his fellow scientists, who are collecting samples to take back to their own planet. He is befriended until they return by a little boy (Elliott), who is lonely after his parents' recent divorce and doesn't have many friends at school. Spielberg's own parents separated when he was a teenager, right after they moved to California. "Divorce," he has said, "was the first scary word I remember hearing." In *E.T.*, "I'm reacting to a situation in my life. When my father left, I went from tormentor to protector with my family. I'd never assumed responsibility for anything except making my home movies. . . . I had become the man of the house." He has also said that Elliott is "not me but he's the closest thing to my experiences in life, growing up in suburbia."

E.T. marked a change in Spielberg's working style. "It's the most emotionally complicated film I've ever made and the least technically complicated," he has said. As a result, for the first time he shot without the aid of storyboards. "Using the script is the best storyboard I had, and everything else from that would be the ideas I would get from blocking a scene, looking at a set. I wasn't thinking five shots ahead. . . . I was thinking to perhaps only the next shot, but it's been better for this movie, which has so much emotion in it."

The reviews of the film were ecstatic and it set box office records, topping even *Star Wars*. There also are fifty merchandise licensing deals tied to it for everything from E.T. pajamas to E.T. bubble gum, which are expected to gross another $1 billion.

E.T. has also affected Spielberg's personal life. In early 1980 his four-year romance with the actress Amy Irving unexpectedly ended for reasons neither will discuss. Since then, Spielberg has dated a number of women, but he now seems to have settled in with Kathleen Carey, who works in the record business. After making *E.T.*, he has said, "I have this deep yearning now to become a father."

For the future, professionally, he has talked about sequels to *Close Encounters* and *E.T.* and a film he has called his *Annie Hall*—a loose remake of a 1943 love-triangle story called *A Guy Named Joe*. In January 1983 he also began filming a sequel to *Raiders*. Spielberg used to say that he didn't want his own studio. ("I have enough trouble directing movies. I don't want to be an emperor of high finance.") But recently he talked about forming a company that would be "like a children's crusade of filmmakers. The only way you can get into this company is if you haven't made a film before."

Even so, it is unlikely that Steven Spielberg will move far away from the camera. For him, filmmaking itself will always be paramount. He has described himself as a "hardworking drone. I enjoy making the movies: getting up early, having to struggle and fight the weather and fight egos and all the things that are always plotting against the completion of a project. I enjoy rolling up my sleeves and getting into it."

Blacks and Women in Hollywood

IF IT IS EXTREMELY hard to become a Hollywood director, it is ten times harder for blacks and women. For them, it is not so much a question of making personal films as of making films at all. The explanation is simple: money. "Filmmaking," Charlton Heston once said, "is the only art form where the artist can't afford his own materials." The money today is in the hands of the white male executives of the major studios.

Strangely, both blacks and women have a long history in filmmaking. An independent black film industry began in the 1920s, producing films by, about, and for blacks. They were made on tiny budgets and shown in the segregated black theaters of the South and the ghetto theaters of the North. Some of them dealt with issues of color and caste, illegitimate children, and historical events; others just mimicked white movies.

Most of the more than one hundred black film companies lasted only long enough to make a few films. The depression, the coming of sound, and the few all-black Hollywood productions finally wiped out all but one. Oscar Micheaux, called the dean of black filmmakers, continued to make films until his death in 1957. He was the producer, director, writer, editor, business manager, and promoter of about fifteen features.

Not until the late 1960s and the early 1970s did black film

directors become active again. In 1969, *Cotton Comes to Harlem* became the first commercially successful film by a black director. Ossie Davis, the actor and stage director, had financed the wild detective comedy independently. When it made $7 million, Hollywood began to sense a lucrative "new" black market.

In 1971, Melvin Van Peebles wrote, directed, produced, scored, and starred in an even more profitable movie—*Sweet Sweetback's Baadasssss Song*. Filled with coarse, realistic street language, it was the story of the radicalization of a black man. Now the studios jumped on the bandwagon with *Shaft*, *Blacula*, *Superfly*, and others. At the peak, in 1973, there were more than one hundred films aimed at the black audience.

While *Sweetback* sprang from an authentic black sensibility, many of the other new "black" films were just standard action scripts with black actors plugged in. They had weak plots, poor craftsmanship, and offensive amounts of violence and sex. They were made quickly and cheaply (for $500,000 to $800,000), but they grossed millions. Unfortunately, although they provided jobs for black writers, directors, actors, and technicians, most of the profits went to the whites who financed, produced, and distributed them.

Black critics and the black community began to object almost immediately to the aesthetic and social values of these so-called blaxploitation films, which glorified the drug culture and the lives of pimps and prostitutes. By 1975, partly because of this pressure but also because of the rising cost of making movies and the failure of *The Wiz*, the $30 million all-black film, these films had almost disappeared. The studios concluded that they didn't need black films to attract black audiences.

Today Sidney Poitier and Michael Schultz are the only black directors who work regularly on black and nonblack films, and neither is considered to have a strong authorial voice. Poitier directed *Buck and the Preacher*, *A Warm December*, *Uptown Saturday Night*, *Let's Do It Again*, *Stir Crazy*, and *Hanky*

Panky. Schultz directed *Cooley High*, *Which Way Is Up?*, *Carwash*, *Greased Lightning*, *Sergeant Pepper's Lonely Hearts Club Band*, and *Carbon Copy*.

Women, too, were active filmmakers in the era of silent film. There were more women directors in Hollywood during the 1910s and 1920s than in any period since. Approximately twenty-six women directors were working for small independent film companies, and women were involved in every aspect of filmmaking. But with the coming of sound and the increased cost of making films, these companies were wiped out by the major studios, and the number of women directors decreased sharply.

Two survivors were Dorothy Arzner and Ida Lupino. Arzner directed seventeen films between 1927 and 1943 and was one of the top ten Hollywood directors in the 1930s. Lupino made eight films through her own production company between 1949 and 1954.

It was not until the late 1960s, however, with the increased use of 16-millimeter film, that women began to appear again as producers, directors, writers, editors, and cinematographers. They began to slip into the documentary field, where the budgets were small.

Studio executives over the years have given numerous excuses for the absence of female directors, even from television, where many male directors get their training. Women don't have the technical skills, the executives claim; they can't control male crews; they don't have the physical stamina; they are stubborn and inflexible; they make messagey films.

The first woman to overcome these prejudices in the 1970s was Elaine May, who had already proved herself salable as a comedian. She directed *A New Leaf* and *The Heartbreak Kid*. Then *Mikey* and *Nicky*, which she brought in late and over budget after two agonizing years of editing, was a critical and financial disaster. This experience not only drove her from filmmaking, but also hurt the prospects of other female directors.

Several women have had a shot at Hollywood since then, but they have yet to follow up on it: Lee Grant (*Tell Me a Riddle*), Joan Tewkesbury (*Old Boyfriends*), Jane Wagner (*Moment to Moment*), Anne Bancroft (*Fatso*), and Joan Darling (*First Love*). Claudia Weill, whose independent feature *Girl Friends* was hailed at Cannes and was bought for distribution by Warner Brothers, then got $7 million to direct *It's My Turn*.

Joan Micklin Silver, however, is the only woman who has had real critical and financial success directing features in the 1970s. Her three films are *Hester Street*, *Between the Lines*, and *Chilly Scenes of Winter*.

Both blacks and women are much better represented in the independent film movement than in Hollywood. Blacks still have less access to television screenings, art houses, and museums, but the number of women independents is about equal to the number of men. Claudia Weill, however, does not see the answer here. She said she could never again make a film financed primarily by grants and loans: "I couldn't ask those kinds of favors again of my friends, to work for so little and on deferrals. . . . If, in fact, you want to make features, you pretty much—after making one like that—are forced to work within the system, because there's no middle territory."

Perhaps, then, the best hope for the future lies in two other directions—with the increasing number of women in the management of the studios, and with the new video technologies, which should provide more opportunities for all filmmakers.

Selected Bibliography

The information in this book came from many sources: general books on American film in the 1970s, books about individual filmmakers, and hundreds of articles in newspapers, general-interest magazines, and specialized film magazines. Listed below are books on film in general. Then, by filmmaker, are books about each and a selection of the pertinent magazine and newspaper articles.

GENERAL BOOKS

GELMIS, JOSEPH. *The Film Director as Superstar*. New York: Doubleday, 1970.

JACOBS, DIANE. *Hollywood Renaissance*. New York: Dell (Delta), 1980.

MONACO, JAMES. *American Film Now: The People, The Power, The Money, The Movies*. New York: New American Library, 1979.

MYLES, LYNDA, and MICHAEL PYE. *The Movies Brats: How the Film Generation Took Over Hollywood*. New York: Holt, Rinehart & Winston, 1979.

WOODY ALLEN

BOOKS

GUTHRIE, LEE. *Woody Allen: A Biography*. New York: Drake, 1978.

HIRSCH, FOSTER. *Love, Sex, Death, and the Meaning of Life: Woody Allen's Comedy*. New York: McGraw-Hill, 1981.

JACOBS, DIANE. . . . *but we need the eggs: The Magic of Woody Allen*. New York: St. Martin's, 1982.

LAX, ERIC. *On Being Funny: Woody Allen and Comedy*. New York: Charterhouse, 1975.

YACOWAR, MAURICE. *Loser Take All: The Comic Art of Woody Allen*. New York: Frederick Ungar, 1979.

ARTICLES

GITTELSON, NATALIE. "The Maturing of Woody Allen." *New York Times Magazine*, April 22, 1979.

HALBERSTADT, IRA. "Scenes from a Mind." *Take One*, November 1978.

KROLL, JACK. "Woody." *Newsweek*, April 24, 1978.

RICH, FRANK. "An Interview with Woody Allen." *Time*, April 30, 1979.

SCHICKEL, RICHARD. "The Basic Woody Allen Joke." *New York Times Magazine*, April 24, 1978.

ROBERT ALTMAN

BOOK

KASS, JUDITH M. *Robert Altman: American Innovator*. New York: Popular Library, 1978.

ARTICLES

ALTMAN, ROBERT. "Interview." *Playboy*, August 1976.

CUTTS, JOHN. "M-A-S-H, McCloud, and McCabe: An Interview with Robert Altman." *Films and Filming*, November 1971.

GRIGSBY, WAYNE. "Robert Altman: A Young Turk at 54." *Maclean's*, April 23, 1979.

GROSS, LARRY. "An Interview with Robert Altman on the Set of 'Nashville.'" *Millimeter*, February 1975.

HARMETZ, ALJEAN. "The 15th Man Who Was Asked to Direct 'M*A*S*H' (and Did) Makes a Peculiar Western." *New York Times Magazine*, June 20, 1971.

MEL BROOKS

BOOKS

ADLER, BILL, and JEFFREY FEINMAN. *Mel Brooks: The Irreverent Funnyman*. Chicago: Playboy Press, 1976.

HOLTZMAN, WILLIAM. *Seesaw: A Dual Biography of Anne Bancroft and Mel Brooks*. New York: Doubleday, 1979.

YACOWAR, MAURICE. *In Method Madness: The Comic Art of Mel Brooks*. New York: St. Martin's, 1981.

ARTICLES

BROOKS, MEL. "Interview." *Playboy*, February 1975.

RIVLIN, ROBERT. "Comedy Director: Interview with Mel Brooks." *Millimeter*, October 1977.

RIVLIN, ROBERT. "Mel Brooks on 'High Anxiety.'" *Millimeter*, December 1977.

TYNAN, KENNETH. "Frolics and Detours of a Short Hebrew Man." *New Yorker*, October 30, 1978.

ZIMMERMAN, PAUL D. "Mad, Mad Mel Brooks." *Newsweek*, February 17, 1975.

FRANCIS COPPOLA

BOOKS

COPPOLA, ELEANOR. *Notes*. New York: Pocket Books, 1979.

JOHNSON, ROBERT K. *Francis Ford Coppola*. Boston: Twyane, 1978.

ARTICLES

BRAUDY, SUSAN. "Francis Ford Coppola: A Profile." *Atlantic*, August, 1976.

DE PALMA, BRIAN. "The Making of 'The Conversation.'" *Filmmakers Newsletter*, May 1974.

FARBER, STEPHEN. "Coppola and 'The Godfather.'" *Sight and Sound*, Autumn 1972.

HALLER, SCOT. "Francis Coppola's Biggest Gamble." *Saturday Review*, July 1981.

ROSS, LILLIAN. "Some Figures on a Fantasy." *New Yorker*, November 8, 1982.

BRIAN DE PALMA

ARTICLES

AMERICAN FILM INSTITUTE. "Brian De Palma: An AFI Seminar on His Work," part 1, no. 43 (April 4, 1973). Beverly Hills, 1977.

BARTHOLOMEW, D. "De Palma of the Paradise." *Cinefantastique*, vol. 4, no. 2 (1975).

DE PALMA, BRIAN. "Brian De Palma: A Day in the Life." *Esquire*, October 1980.

DUNNING, JENNIFER. "Brian De Palma: 'I Operate on the Principle of Escalating Terror.'" *New York Times*, April 23, 1978.

KAKUTANI, MICHIKO. "De Palma: 'I'm Much More of a Romantic Than Hitchcock.' " *New York Times*, July 19, 1981.

GEORGE LUCAS

ARTICLES

FARBER, STEPHEN. "George Lucas: The Skinky Kid Hits the Big Time." *Film Quarterly*, Spring 1974.

HARMETZ, ALJEAN. "The Saga beyond 'Star Wars.'" *New York Times*, May 15, 1980.

LUCAS, GEORGE, interviewed by Mitch Tuchman and Anne Thompson. "I'm the Boss." *Film Comment*, July–August 1981.

O'QUINN, KERRY. "The George Lucas Saga," Chapters 1 and 2. *Starlog*, July and August, 1981.

SHERMAN, STRATFORD P. "The Empire Pays Off." *Fortune*, October 6, 1980.

PAUL MAZURSKY

ARTICLES

AMERICAN FILM INSTITUTE. "Paul Mazursky." *Dialogue on Film*, November, 1974.

APPELBAUM, RALPH. "Experience and Expression: Paul Mazursky." *Films and Filming*, August 1978.

GREENFIELD, JEFF. "Paul Mazursky in Wonderland." *Life*, September 4, 1970.

HALLER, SCOT. "Happily Married Man Who Examines the Shaky State of Marriage." *Horizon*, May 1978.

MONACO, JAMES. "Paul Mazursky and *Willie and Phil*." *American Film*, July –August 1980.

MARTIN SCORSESE

BOOK

KELLY, MARY PAT. *Martin Scorsese: The First Decade*. Pleasantville, N.Y.: Redgrave, 1980.

ARTICLES

AMERICAN FILM INSTITUTE. "Martin Scorsese." *Dialogue on Film*, April 1975.

FLATLEY, GUY. "Martin Scorsese's Gamble." *New York Times Magazine*, February 8, 1976.

HOWARD, STEVE. "The Making of 'Alice Doesn't Live Here Anymore': An Interview with Director Martin Scorsese." *Filmmakers Newsletter*, March 1975.

ROSEN, MARJORIE. "The New Hollywood: Martin Scorsese." *Film Comment*, March–April 1975.

WEINER, THOMAS. "Martin Scorsese Fights Back." *American Film*, November 1980.

STEVEN SPIELBERG

ARTICLES

AMERICAN FILM INSTITUTE. "Steven Spielberg: An AFI Seminar on His Work," part 1, nos. 170–71 (November 14, 1973; November 26, 1975). Beverly Hills, 1977.

CORLISS, RICHARD. "Steve's Summer Magic." *Time*, May 31, 1982.

JANOS, LEO. "Steven Spielberg: L'Enfant Directeur." *Cosmopolitan*, June 1980.

SWIRES, STEVE. "Filming the Fantastic: Steven Spielberg." *Starlog*, October 1978.

TUCHMAN, MITCH. "Spielberg's Close Encounter." *Film Comment*, January–February 1978.

BLACKS AND WOMEN IN HOLLYWOOD

BOOKS

CRIPPS, T. R. *Black Film as Genre*. Bloomington: Indiana University Press, 1978.

SMITH, SHARON. *Women Who Make Movies*. New York: Hopkinson & Blake, 1975.

ARTICLES

DAVIS, SALLY OGLE. "The Struggle of Women Directors." *New York Times Magazine*, January 11, 1981.

WEAVER, HAROLD D., JR. "Black Filmmakers in Africa and America." *Sightlines*, Spring 1976.

For research on American filmmakers, two invaluable guides to periodicals are available in many public libraries: *Film Literature Index* and *International Index to Film Periodicals*.

For just keeping up, *American Film* (published by the American Film Institute, John F. Kennedy Center for the Performing Arts, Washington, D.C. 20556) and *Film Comment* (published by the Film Society of Lincoln Center, 140 W. 65 St., New York, N.Y. 10023) are very good sources of information about people and issues important in film today. Both magazines can be found in many public libraries and are available by subscription.

Index

About the Author

DIAN G. SMITH is a freelance writer with a master's degree in education from Harvard University. She is the author of *Careers in the Visual Arts: Talking with Professionals* and *Women in Finance*, and her articles have appeared in *Self*, *Glamour*, *3-2-1 Contact* (Children's Television Workshop), the *Christian Science Monitor*, the *Chronicle of Higher Education*, and other national publications.

Her interest in film is long-standing and she comes by it naturally, for her great-aunt, Annie Warner Robins, was a sister of the Warner brothers.